DATE DUE			

THE
SCIENCE
OF
MAN

An Illustrated
Introduction to Anthropology

BY ASHLEY MONTAGU

Illustrated by Robert J. Lee

AN ODYSSEY SURVEY BOOK

© Copyright 1964 by Ashley Montagu.
All rights reserved.
Printed in the U.S.A. by
Western Printing & Lithographing Company.
Published by
Odyssey Press, Inc., New York.

Library of Congress Catalog Card Number: 64-14671

Cover and book design by Walter Brooks.

To the Memory of

Božo Škerlj

PREFACE

This book has been designed to be helpful to the general reader in gaining an understanding of the origin and evolution of the species of which he is a member. Text, tables, and illustrations have all been specially prepared for this book in the service of the reader; for, the proper understanding of the factors which have been at work in making man, in all his remarkable variety—what he has been and what he has become—should constitute an indispensable part of the mental equipment of everyone living in the modern world.

A knowledge of the basic facts of anthropology are not only fascinating in themselves, but are of immediate practical use in a world which is rapidly shrinking and which is daily confronted with problems which a knowledge of the facts of anthropology can help to solve. I hope the reader will find the book practically useful as well as interesting in itself.

The making of a book such as this calls upon the special skills of a large number of persons. I should like to thank all those who have been so helpful in the production of this book. Mr. Richard Fisher my original editor, Mrs. Sybil Taylor my continuing editor, Mr. Robert Lee who is responsible for the excellent illustrations, Mr. Walter Brooks the designer of the book, and Mrs. Elizabeth Green who was most helpful with the technical details of layout. I am most grateful to my friend Professor James Deetz of the University of California at Santa Barbara for his assistance in the making of Table VIII. Thanks also are due to Linda and Don Miller for their help with Table IX.

ASHLEY MONTAGU

Princeton, New Jersey
February 1964

Man and His Works

What an astonishing and excitingly interesting creature is man! On the pages of this book are shown something of the variety of man and of his works. From an apelike artificer of wood, bone, and stone tools, living in small wandering bands made up of a few families, subsisting by food-gathering and hunting, with no permanent habitation, man has developed in such a manner that he now commands the energy of the atom.

The forms and the diversities of his ways of life constitute a never-ending source of wonderment and enchantment. How did that variety of form and diversity of life come about? By what processes, biological, environmental, physical, and social, were the differences *and* the likenesses, physical and social, produced? By what routes has man traversed the long journey through time which have brought him to his present high peak of physical and social development? What are the processes which maintain, and

Achelous, great river god of Greeks.
An Etruscan pendant, Sixth Century B.C.

what are those that bring about the changes in, the physical and social traits of different populations?

These questions, the endeavor to answer them, and to systema tize the answers, constitute the subject-matter of *Anthropology,* the science of man.

CLASSIFICATION

The orderly classification of living things (sometimes called taxonomy, Greek: *taxis,* arrangement, and *nomos,* a law) has one principal purpose: to provide a simple practical means by which students of any group may know what they are talking about, and others may find out. Reference to Table II showing the classification of the primates will at once make clear that names given to suborders and superfamilies usually terminate in "oidea," the

GEOLOGICAL TIME SCALE OF THE APPEARANCE OF VARIOUS REPRESENTATIVE FORMS OF LIFE

TABLE I.

Era	Period	Epoch	Millions of years since the beginning of each epoch	Forms of Life
CENOZOIC The Age of Mammals	Quaternary	Recent	1/40	Man, the slave and master.
CENOZOIC The Age of Mammals	Quaternary	Pleistocene	1-2	*Zinjanthropus, Pithecanthropus, Sinanthropus, Swanscombe, Homo sapiens.*
CENOZOIC The Age of Mammals	Tertiary	Pliocene	12	*Kenyapithecus.* First men probably appeared during the latter part of this epoch.
CENOZOIC The Age of Mammals	Tertiary	Miocene	28	Appearance of true anthropoid apes. *Dryopithecus, Sivapithecus, Proconsul.*
CENOZOIC The Age of Mammals	Tertiary	Oligocene	39	Primitive anthropoid apes appear such as *Propliopithecus.*
CENOZOIC The Age of Mammals	Tertiary	Eocene	58	Spread of modern mammals. Tarsiers.
CENOZOIC The Age of Mammals	Tertiary	Paleocene	75	Appearance of insectivorous preprimates and earliest primates, primitive lemuroids and tarsioids.
MESOZOIC The Age of Reptiles	Secondary	Cretaceous	135	Rise of archaic mammals and birds. Extinction of dinosaurs, pterodactyls, and toothed birds. Insectivores.
MESOZOIC The Age of Reptiles	Secondary	Jurassic	165	Spread of primitive mammals and pterodactyls, rise of toothed birds.
MESOZOIC The Age of Reptiles	Secondary	Triassic	205	Rise of dinosaurs, pterodactyls, and primitive mammals.
PALEOZOIC The Age of Ancient Life		Permian	230	Spread of amphibians and insects. Extinction of trilobites.
PALEOZOIC The Age of Ancient Life		Carboniferous	255	Primitive reptiles, insects, spiders. Great forests of ferns and mosses.
PALEOZOIC The Age of Ancient Life		Devonian	325	Rise of fishes and amphibians. Spreading of forests.
PALEOZOIC The Age of Ancient Life		Silurian	360	Rise of ostracoderms, sea-scorpions (Eurypterids). First land plants.
PALEOZOIC The Age of Ancient Life		Ordovician	425	First primitive fishes, the ostracoderms.
PALEOZOIC The Age of Ancient Life		Cambrian	505	Still no land-life known, trilobites, mollusks, brachiopods.
PROTEROZOIC			925	Sponges, protozoöns, diatoms, and protophyta, and other commencing complex forms of life developed during this era.
ARCHEOZOIC			1,500	Probably simple unicellular sea-dwelling forms.

The estimated number of millions of years in the fourth column for the Tertiary period is based upon a combination of paleontological data, with specific reference to the evolution of the horse from *Hyracotherium* to *Equus,* and the evidence of geology and radioactivity. The figures for the preceding periods are largely based on the uranium transformation method. When uranium and lead occur together in a fragment of rock otherwise free from these elements, it may generally be safely assumed that the lead represents "decomposed" or transformed uranium. It is known that 1,000,000 grams of uranium yields 1/7600 grams of lead a year. Hence the age of such rocks can be determined from the proportions of these elements which they contain, thus:

$$\text{Age of rock} = \frac{\text{Weight of Lead}}{\text{Weight of Uranium}} \times 7600 \text{ million years}$$

termination "idae" is appended to family names, and those bestowed on subfamilies end in "inae." It was the Swedish naturalist, Carl von Linné, better known by his Latin name, Carolus Linnaeus, who, in his famous book, *Systema Naturae* (1735, and in a second edition 1758), devised the nomenclature and the classificatory system we use today. Proper names are used for genera, and the species name always follows that of the genus, and the name of the subspecies follows that of the species. The name of the genus begins with a capital letter, while the names of species and subspecies begin with a small letter, and each name is always italicized, as for example, *Gorilla gorilla beringei*, that is the genus *Gorilla*, the species *gorilla*, and the subspecies *beringei*. Thus, for example, man belongs to the:

Kingdom:	Animalia
Phylum:	Chordata
Class:	Mammalia
Order:	Primates
Suborder:	Anthropoidea
Infraorder:	Catarrhini
Superfamily:	Hominoidea
Family:	Hominidae
Genus:	*Homo*
Species:	*sapiens*

Man's place in nature is among the *class* of Mammalia and the *order* of Primates. Mammals derive their name from and are char-

Tree-shrew *(Urogale everetti).*

acterized by the fact that they suckle their young with milk produced by the mammary glands of the mother, possess a four-chambered heart, breathe by air reoxygenated in the lungs, and have a growth of hair over the body. Sixteen living orders of mammals are recognized, of which the two most important in the study of the origin and evolution of man are the Insectivora, consisting of such creatures as shrews, moles, and hedgehogs, and the Primates, comprising the lemurs, monkeys, apes, and men.

The insectivores are of interest to us because, including as they do the ancestors of all placental mammals, one of their families constitutes the ancestral group which gave rise to the Primates. This family, the Tupaiidae, or oriental tree shrews, comprises 6 genera, 32 species, and about 100

TOP: Ring-tailed Lemur *(Lemur catta).*

MIDDLE: Marmoset *(Leontocebus rosalia).*

BOTTOM: Tarsier *(Tarsius syrichta).*

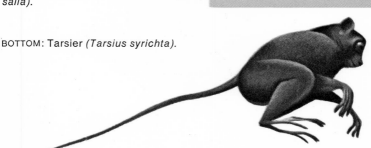

Sub-order	Infra-order and Series	Super-family	Family	Subfamily	Genus	Common Name
PROSIMII	Lemuriformes	Lemuroidea	Lemuridae	Lemurinae	*Lemur* *Hapalemur* *Lepilemur*	True Lemurs Gentle Lemurs Sportive Lemurs
				Cheirogaleinae	*Cheirogaleus* *Microcebus* *Phaner*	Dwarf Lemurs Mouse Lemurs Fork-Crowned Dwarf Lemurs
			Indriidae		*Indris* *Propithecus* *Lichanotus*	Endrina Sifaka Woolly Avahi
			Daubentoniidae		*Daubentonia*	Aye-Aye
	Lorisiformes		Lorisdae	Lorisinae	*Loris* *Nycticebus* *Arctocebus* *Perodicticus*	Slender Loris Slow Loris Angwantibo Potto
			Galagidae	Galaginae	*Galago* *Galagoides* *Euoticus*	Typical Bush Babies Dwarf Bush Babies Needle-Clawed Bush Babies
	Tarsii-formes	Tarsi-oidea	Tarsiidae		*Tarsius*	Tarsier
ANTHROPOIDEA	Platyrrhini	Ceboidea	Callithricidae	Callithricinae	*Callithrix* *Cebuella* *Mico* *Marikina* *Tamarin* *Tamarinus* *Leontocebus* *Oedipomidas*	Tufted Marmoset Pygmy Marmoset Naked-eared Marmoset Bald-headed Tamarin Black-faced Tamarin Mustached Tamarin Maned Tamarin Pinché
			Cebidae	Callimiconinae	*Callimico*	Goeldi's Monkey
				Aotinae	*Aotes* *Callicebus*	Night Monkey Titi Monkey
				Pitheciinae	*Pithecia* *Chiropotes* *Cacajao*	Hairy Saki Monkey Short-haired Saki Ouakári Monkey
				Cebinae	*Saimiri* *Cebus*	Squirrel Monkey Capuchin Monkey
				Atelinae	*Lagothrix* *Ateles* *Brachyteles*	Woolly Monkey Spider Monkey Woolly Spider Monkey
				Alouattinae	*Alouatta*	Howler Monkey
	Catarrhini	Ceropithecoidea	Cercopithecidae	Cercopithecinae	*Cercopithecus* *Erythrocebus* *Cercocebus* *Macaca* *Cynopithecus* *Theropithecus* *Papio* *Mandrillus*	Guenons Red-haired Patas Mangabey Macaque Celebes or Black Ape Gelada Baboon Typical Baboon Mandrill and Drill
				Semnopithecinae	*Semnopithecus* *Colobus* *Rhinopithecus* *Nasalis*	Langur Guereza Snub-nosed Langur Proboscis Monkey
		Hominoidea	Hylobatidae	Hylobatinae	*Hylobates* *Symphalangus*	Common Gibbon Siamang
			Pongidae	Ponginae	*Pongo* *Pan* *Gorilla*	Orang-Utan Chimpanzee Gorilla
			Hominidae		*Homo*	Man

subspecies. Squirrel-like in appearance and mainly terrestrial, they spend most of their time on the ground with the smaller species tending to spend somewhat more time in the trees. The smaller species also tend to be nocturnal in their habits, that is, active during the night and sleeping during the daylight hours; the larger species are diurnal, that is, they sleep at night and are active during the daylight. These arrangements appear to have a protective value. Small-bodied animals are safer from predators during the night, and larger-bodied animals are able to forage for and protect themselves more efficiently during daylight. Hands and feet are adapted for grasping and thumb and big toe are to some extent opposable. All digits are provided with curved claws; the number of teeth on one side of the upper and lower jaw, known as the dental formula, is I 2/3, C 1/1, PM 3/3, M 3/. (The letters I, C, PM and M stand for incisors, canines, premolars, and molars respectively. The numbers at the left of the diagonal refer to one side of the upper jaw, the numbers at the right to one side of the lower jaw. The equivalent opposite side is, of course, identical.) The tail is not prehensile, but is used as a balancing organ. Breeding occurs throughout the year, and usually two, sometimes one, and occasionally up to four, offspring are born.

The tupaioids have the generalized features of a primitive primate which could well have given rise to all the lines which eventually led to the evolution of all other primates. The earliest tupaiods known are from the Paleocene some 75 million years ago. ago.

The order Primates, embracing the lemurs, monkeys, apes, and man, is characterized by the following features: relatively large and complicated brains, hands and feet grasping or clearly derived from grasping type, presence of a collarbone, freely mobile digits, and the presence, usually, of two breasts.

Classification of the Primates is shown in Table II.

The Lemurs are small foxlike creatures ranging in size from a mouse (Cheirogale) to the large endrinas (Indri) with a body-length of 24 inches. They are almost entirely arboreal and nocturnal, and since they appear to have specialized in a direction which led to no other line of Primates, we need not be concerned with them further here.

The Tarsier of the Malay Archipelago, Celebes, and the Philippines, *Tarsius syrichta,* is known as the spectral tarsier because of its enormous eyes and the remarkable elongation of the tarsal bones of the foot which enable it to take gigantic leaps, like a frog. Body length is about 8 inches, with a nonprehensile tail tufted at the tip. Tarsiers are arboreal and nocturnal. Diet is principally insectivorous. The dental formula is I 2/1, C 1/1, PM 3/3, M 3/3. There is no special breeding season, and a single offspring is produced at birth.

In their structural characters the tarsiers make a much closer approach to the monkeys and apes than do the other prosimii (the lemurs, lorises and tarsiers). This is seen in the structure of brain and skull, the reduction in the olfactory organs, in the snout, in the teeth, and in the form of the nose and lips. It is generally believed that the tarsiers gave rise to the New World (Platyrrhini) and Old World (Catarrhini) monkeys and possibly to the gibbons. It was from an Old World monkey stock that the early anthropoids arose, and from these, in turn, that the line which led to man came into being.

The New World monkeys, or platyrrhini, range from southern Mexico to Rio Grande do Sul on the border between Brazil and Uruguay. There are two distinct families, the marmosets (Callithricidae) with 8 genera, some 35 species, and some 51 subspecies, and the typical South American monkeys (Cebidae) with 11 genera, 39 species, and some 161 subspecies. The marmosets are small creatures, about the size of squirrels, with a dental formula of I 2/2, C 1/1, PM 3/3, M 2/2. They are arboreal and diurnal in habit, there is no restricted breeding period, and marmosets are the only primates that normally produce more than a single young at birth, the usual number being two or three. Interestingly enough, the young are generally carried by the father, the mother receiving them for the purpose of nursing. Frequently the care of the young is left to its older siblings. The brain is relatively remarkably large, but is still unconvoluted. The marmosets are presumed to be capable of some stereoscopic vision.

The South American monkeys, or Cebidae, are larger in size than the marmosets, but not, on the whole, as large as the Old World monkeys. All the digits bear nails, with the exception of the first; the thumb is not opposable but is used as a finger; the tail is prehensile in only half the genera (*Cebus, Lagothrix, Brachyteles*, and *Alouatta*). In the two genera of spider monkeys, *Ateles* and *Brachyteles*, the thumb is reduced to a nailless tubercle. The muz-

Gibbon *(Hylobates lar)*.

zle is less projecting than in the Old World monkeys, and the surface of the brain is richly convoluted. With the exception of the night monkeys, *Aotes*, all the Cebidae are diurnal, and all are arboreal and capable of stereoscopic vision, and probably also of color vision. There is no definite breeding season and one young is born at a birth. The dental formula is I 2/2, C 1/1, PM 3/3, M 3/3.

The Old World monkeys or Cercopithecidae are African and Asiatic in their distribution, with the exception of the Barbary Ape *(Macaca sylvana)* which is the only European monkey, having long been a resident of the rock of Gibraltar in Europe. There are 12 genera, 88 species, and some 245 subspecies. The New and the Old World monkeys originated from a common stock and though separated by a time span of some 50 million years, they developed in remarkably similar form. One marked difference, however, is that the Old World monkeys have lost a premolar tooth, and they have the dental formula which is also that of apes and man, namely I 2/2, C 1/1, PM 2/2, M 3/3. Also, thumb and big toe are opposable, all digits have flattened nails, and the tail is not

RESEMBLANCES AND DIFFERENCES BETWEEN THE VARIOUS KINDS OF PRIMATES

TABLE III.

Trait or Character	Lemurs	Tarsiers	New World Monkeys Marmosets	New World Monkeys Ceboids	Old World Monkeys	Gibbon	Orangutan	Chimpanzee	Gorilla	Man
Habitat	Madagascar, Africa and Asia	Malay Archipelago, Philippines	Mexico and South America	South America	Africa and Asia	Asia and Malaysia	Borneo and Sumatra	Central Africa	Central Africa	Global
Number of Genera	18	1	8	11	12	2	1	1	1	1
Number of Species	34	3	35	39	88	7	2	1	1	1
Number of Subspecies	100	12	51	161	245	22	0	2	2	0
First Sexual Skin (in years)	None	*	Present	None	2 years 6 months	None	Present in some during pregnancy	8 years	Absent	Absent
First Menstruation (in years)	Absent	Present	Non-menstrual bleeding	Present	2 years 10 months	8 years 6 months	Present	8 years 11 months	9 years 6 months	13½
Duration of Menstruation (in days)	Absent	Absent	*	1-5	5	2½	*	4	4	5
Duration of Menstrual Cycle (in days)	*	26	*	*	27	30	29	35	30	28
Time of Ovulation (counting from first day of menses)	*	*	*	*	13	*	*	14	14	14
Breeding Season	March-June	Unrestricted	Unrestricted	Unrestricted	Unrestricted	Unrestricted	Unrestricted	Unrestricted	Unrestricted	Unrestricted
Interval Between First Menstruation and First Conception	*	*	*	*	1 year 6 months	*	*	1 year 3 months	1 year 6 months	3 years
Duration of Pregnancy (in days)	125	*	145	139	170	210	275	231	259	266½
Duration of Labor (in hours)	*	*	*	*	3½	*	*	5	*	First child 14 Later children 8
Birth Weight (in percentage of adult female weight)	4.6	*	*	7.0-8.5	4.6-7.0	7.5	4.1	4.0	2.4	5.5
Care of Infant	Mother	Mother	Father	Mother usually	Mother	Mother	Mother	Mother	Mother	Mother
Suckling (in months)	6+	Several	Several	Several	6+	6+	36+	24+	36+	12+
Multiple Births	Less frequent than single	Rarely	Usual	Occasionally	About 1.05%	Rarely	Very rare	6% in captivity	Very rare	1.1%
Completion of Permanent Dentition	*	*	*	6 years	6 years 10 months	9 years	9 years 8 months	10 years 2 months	10 years 6 months	19 years 9 months
Life Span (in years)	14	*	10	14	25	30	30	35	35	75
Brain Weight (in grams)	30	3.6	10	45-112	60-200	96	371	345	425	1320
Brain Weight/Body Weight Ratio	13.5	39	39	10-70	12-30	21	5.4	12	4.7	

Stereoscopic Vision	Absent	Doubtful	Some	Present	Present	Present	Present	Present	Present	Present
Color Vision	Doubtful	Doubtful	Doubtful	Present	Present	Present	Present	Present	Present	Present
Habitus and Waking Activity	Mostly nocturnal	Nocturnal	Diurnal	Mostly diurnal	Mostly Diurnal	Diurnal	Diurnal	Mainly Diurnal	Diurnal	Diurnal
Mode of Life	Mainly arboreal	Arboreal and Terrestrial	Arboreal	Arboreal	Mainly arboreal	Arboreal	Arboreal	Mainly Terrestrial	Terrestrial	Terrestrial
Social Aggregates	Family groups	Family groups	Family groups	Small communities	Small communities	Small bands	Family groups	Small bands	Small bands	Large groups
Shelter	In trees	At base of bushes	In trees	In trees	Mostly in trees	In trees	Nests in trees	Lower branches of trees	Lower branches of trees	In roofed buildings
Diet	Frugivorous	Insectivorous	Frugivorous and insectivorous	Mainly frugivorous	Mainly frugivorous	Vegetarian insects, and small birds	Frugivorous	Frugivorous	Herbivorous	Omnivorous
Locomotion	Quadrupeds	Leaping	Climbing	Climbing	Climbing	Brachiation	Brachiation	Obliquely quadrupedal	Obliquely quadrupedal	Bipedal
Height or Length	4–24 inches	8 inches	10 inches	10–30 inches	12–35 inches	3 feet	4 feet	5 feet	5 feet 6 inches	5 feet 6 inches
Weight (in pounds)	5	$\frac{1}{2}$	$\frac{1}{2}$	20	20	13	♂ 165, ♀ 81	♂ 110, ♀ 88	♂ 375, ♀ 200	♂ 150, ♀ 130
Dental Formula	$I^2_2, C^1_1, PM^3_3, M^3_3$	$I^2_2, C^1_1, PM^3_3, M^3_3$	$I^2_2, C^1_1, PM^3_3, M^2_2$	$I^2_2, C^1_1, PM^3_3, M^3_3$	$I^2_2, C^1_1, PM^2_2, M^3_3$	$I^2_2, C^1_1, PM^2_2, M^3_3$	$I^2_2, C^1_1, PM^2_2, M^3_3$	$I^2_2, C^1_1, PM^2_2, M^3_3$	$I^2_2, C^1_1, PM^2_2, M^3_3$	$I^2_2, C^1_1, PM^2_2, M^3_3$
Length of Hindlimbs Compared to Forelimbs	Hind limbs longer than forelimbs	Hindlimbs longer than forelimbs	Hindlimbs much longer	Hindlimbs usually longer	Hindlimbs longer than forelimbs	Forelimbs much longer	Forelimbs much longer	Forelimbs longer	Forelimbs longer	Hindlimbs longer
Thumb Length in Percentage Proportion to Hand Length	46	*	50	50	56	54	44	47	50	68
Thumb	Opposable	Opposable	Not opposable	Not opposable	Opposable	Opposable	Opposable	Opposable	Opposable	Opposable
Big Toe	Opposable	Opposable	Opposable	Opposable	Opposable	Opposable	Opposable	Opposable	Opposable	Not opposable
Nails or Claws	Nails except on 2nd toe	Nails except on 2nd and 3rd toes	Claws except big toe	Nails	Nails	Nails	Nails	Nails	Nails	Nails
Tympanic External Auditory Meatus	Absent	Present	Present	Absent	Present	Present	Present	Present	Present	Present
Nostrils	Widely separated	Widely separated	Widely separated	Widely separated	Narrowly separated	Narrowly separated	Narrowly separated	Narrowly separated	Narrowly separated	Narrowly separated
Laryngeal Sacs	Absent	Absent	Absent	Absent	Absent	Mostly in symphalangus	Present	Present	Present	Absent
Pterion	Parieto-sphenoidal	Protomalar parieto-sphenoidal	Malar-parieto-sphenoidal	Malar-parieto-sphenoidal	Mostly fronto-temporal	Spheno-parietal	Mostly spheno-parietal	Fronto-temporal	Fronto-temporal	Spheno-parietal
Lacrimal Foramen	External	External	Internal	Internal	Internal	Internal	Internal	Internal	Internal	Internal
Entepicondylar Foramen	Present	Present	Present	Present	Absent	Absent	Absent	Absent	Absent	Absent
Chromosome Number	44–60	80	46	44–54	42–72	44	48	48	48	46
Ischial Callosities	Absent	Absent	Absent	Absent	Present	Present	In 5%	In 38%	7%	Absent
Tail	Non-prehensile	Non-prehensile	Non-prehensile	Prehensile in half the genera	Non-prehensile	Absent	Absent	Absent	Absent	Absent

*Data not available

Mandrill *(Mandrillus sphinx).*

prehensile. The nostrils tend to be set close together, whereas in the New World monkeys they tend to be more widely separated; visual acuity is highly developed, there is no definite breeding season, and one young is usually born; diet is mainly frugivorous. Most Old World monkeys are arboreal, but some, like the baboons, are terrestrial. All are diurnal.

The apes together with man fall into a natural unit, the super-family Hominoidea. The Hominoidea consists of two families: the Pongidae or anthropoid apes, and the Hominidae or men. The Pongidae consists of the three great apes, the gorilla *(Gorilla)*, the chimpanzee *(Pan)*, and the orang-utan *(Pongo)*. The first two are inhabitants of Equatorial Africa, the orang of Borneo and Sumatra. The fourth ape, the gibbon, is of a very different kind from these, having two genera, the common gibbon *(Hylobates)* of Asia and the siamang *(Symphalangus)* of Sumatra. The gibbons have pursued a very different direction of evolution since the Oligocene, some 40 million years ago, which has been quite independent of the great apes.

Orang-utan *(Pongo pygmaeus).*   Chimpanzee *(Pan troglodytes.)*

The gibbons are slightly under 3 feet in height and are characterized by the extraordinary length of the upper extremities, so
that when they stand erectly the tips of the fingers touch the
ground. The siamang's upper extremities are even longer in proportion to its legs than the gibbon's. The siamang differs from the
common gibbon in being somewhat larger, heavier (24 as compared with 13 pounds), in having a shorter trunk and broader
chest, shorter legs, broader hands, an average cranial capacity of
125 cc. (cubic centimeters) compared with 98 cc., a longer skull,
scantier body hair, and webbing between the second and third
toes. The gibbons are the aerial acrobats of the primate kingdom,
progressing through the trees by overarm swinging (brachiation).
Progression in this manner occurs about 90 per cent of the time;
the remaining 10 per cent of the time is spent in jumping and
walking on the ground. There is no definite breeding season; one
young is born at a birth. Diet is frugivorous and insectivorous,
with occasional small birds and eggs.

A trait in which the gibbons differ consistently from the great

19

apes is in the invariable presence of ischial callosities on their rumps.

The orang-utan (Malay for "wild-man-of-the-woods") consists of a single genus, *Pongo*, and two subspecies, the one inhabiting Borneo and the other the smaller island off the coast of Borneo, Sumatra. The orang attains a height of slightly over 4 feet, the male weighing about 165 pounds and the female about 80 pounds. The coarse shaggy hair is a reddish-brown or bright foxy red. Skin color is pale yellowish-brown. The average cranial capacity is somewhat over 400 cc. There is no definite breeding season, and one young is born at a birth. Orangs are very gentle creatures; they are almost exclusively arboreal and frugivorous in diet.

The chimpanzee consists of a single genus, *Pan*, and one species, *troglodytes*, and is an inhabitant of western and eastern equatorial Africa. The average height of the male is 5 feet and his weight 110 pounds; the female's height is 4 feet and her weight 88 pounds. Chimpanzees are essentially terrestrial creatures, and contrary to common belief they are not very expert even when, on occasion, they do climb a tree. Cranial capacity is about 400 cc. Skin color varies from white, mottled brown, brown, to black. Breeding occurs at all times, and usually there is one offspring at a birth, though in captivity 5 per cent of births recorded have been of twins.

The gorilla is an inhabitant of east central and western equatorial Africa. There is only one genus, *Gorilla*, and one species, *gorilla*, and two subspecies: the western equatorial or lowland or coastal gorilla, *Gorilla gorilla gorilla*, and the east central highland or mountain gorilla, *Gorilla gorilla beringei*. The two subspecies differ from one another in minor ways physically; the mountain gorilla has somewhat shorter arms, broader and shorter hands, usually webbed toes, narrower hips, greater length of trunk, narrower width between the eyes, greater length of neck, generally narrower skull, longer palate, and thicker pelage.

The gorilla is the largest and bulkiest of all the primates. Average height is 5 feet 6 inches, average weight 450 pounds, though weights up to 670 pounds have been recorded. Average chest girth is 56 inches, and skin is usually black. The average cranial capacity of the male is 550 cc., though 650 cc. has been recorded in an adult male gorilla.

The gorilla is a terrestrial creature, and habitually progresses in an obliquely quadrupedal position, with his bent fingers and the

20

full soles of his feet appressed to the ground. His forelimbs are so much longer than his habitually bent hind limbs that the obliquely quadrupedal form of locomotion follows from these anatomical facts. The gorilla is able to stand erectly and even to run a few steps in that position, but that is not his habitual posture. The smaller animals occasionally climb trees in which they progress by brachiation and in other appropriate ways. At night they usually build nests at the foot of trees, sometimes in the lower branches of trees or under rock ledges.

The Apes Summarized

All apes are without tails whereas all monkeys have tails. All apes have both opposable thumbs and big toes, and all of them have flattened nails on their fingers and toes. Some of the monkeys have claws, at least on some of their digits. The great apes are all over 4 feet in height, have brains of 400 cc. and over, and are the most intelligent of the nonhuman primates. The gibbon is the only one of the apes who is under 3 feet in height and has a small brain. All apes are diurnal in their habits, and for the most part vegetarian in their diets, though in captivity they easily adapt themselves to a meat-eating diet. They live in small family bands, the bands together seldom numbering more than 40 to 50 individuals. They are very peaceful creatures. They all have large canine teeth, very unlike those of men, and these teeth are adapted for the purposes of biting into and shredding the bark from young saplings and other plants. Their functions as defensive or offensive weapons have been wrongly overemphasized, their primary purpose being to enable the individual to deal with the otherwise refractory plant materials upon which these apes live. Female orangs have very reduced canine teeth and manage to survive very well without the tusklike canines of the males. The possession of large canine teeth necessitates the presence of a large space or diastema in the upper jaw for the reception of the upper part of the lower canine tooth. This space is called the premaxillary diastema, or simian gap, and all monkeys and apes possess such a diastema. Except for the ape-man of Java, *Pithecanthropus erectus robustus* or *Homo erectus robustus* (see p. 39), man never does. The body of apes is usually overgrown with a thick hairy coat.

None of the living monkeys or apes can be regarded as being ancestors of man. The monkeys are ruled out because man cannot be directly descended from a monkey but must be descended from a very much more advanced form such as an apelike creature, but an apelike creature very much less apelike than any of the living great apes. The living apes are somewhat too specialized, that is to say, overdeveloped in various directions, such as in the canine teeth, the length of the upper extremities, and a great many other features, for man to have descended from them. Indeed, the common ancestors of the great apes and of man flourished in the Miocene some 28 million years ago, and ever since that time the lines which led to the evolution of the great apes on the one hand and of man on the other have maintained their separateness. The great apes and man are not linear relatives but remote collateral relatives, "cousins," neither standing in a linear relation to the

Gorilla *(Gorilla gorilla gorilla).*

other. When it is sometimes said that man is descended from the monkeys, that is true in much the same sense that it is true to say that man is descended from fishes. Certainly man's relationship to the monkeys is much closer than it is to the fishes, but it is still very remote. And when it is said that man is descended from an ape, it should be quite clear that man is not descended from any of the living apes, but from some remote apelike creature.

EARLY FORERUNNERS OF MAN

Proconsulidae. The family of apes of this name are known from some 9 localities in Kenya Colony, and from Kapak in North-eastern Uganda. They flourished in the Lower Miocene some 28 million years ago. Three species have been identified, *Proconsul africanus, Proconsul major,* and *Proconsul nyanzae .* These apes were quadrupedal and did not exceed 3 feet in height, their skulls were without the overhanging brow ridges of modern apes, the jaw narrow with a forward convergence of the tooth rows, large canine and small molar teeth.

The Proconsulidae are of great interest to us, because they show us what an unspecialized ape looked like, one that could have been ancestral on the one hand to the living apes, and on the other to the line which led to man.

Kenyapithecus wickeri. An advanced proconsulid, discovered at

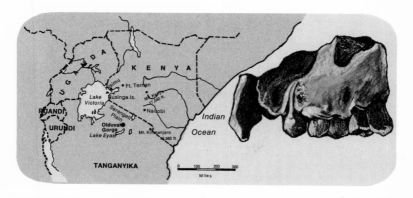

LEFT: sites of important discoveries of fossil man and his precursors in East Africa. RIGHT: *Kenyapithecus wickeri,* East Africa

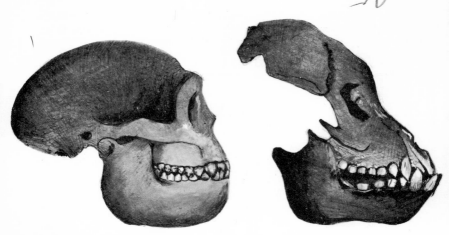

LEFT: *Oreopithecus bambolii,* Italy. RIGHT: *Proconsul africanus,* East Africa

the base of the Pliocene at Fort Ternan, Kenya, in 1962, dates back some 14 million years. *Kenyapithecus wickeri* is represented by a portion of the left side of the upper jaw with the canine tooth, the root of the first premolar, and the complete first and second molars. The canine is quite reduced, and the remaining teeth are quite manlike. There is an absence of the simian gap (premaxillary diastema) between the upper lateral incisor and the canine tooth. There is a canine fossa in the jaw above the root of the canine tooth. These are manlike traits. Yet we can be sure that *Kenyapithecus* had not achieved manlike status because he did not have the necessary brain development. He is, however, a most interesting example of the kind of evolutionary changes that were taking place in the direction of manlike forms.

Oreopithecus bambolii. An early, and apparently unsuccessful experiment, in the direction of manlike development is represented by a fossil form first discovered in the 1860's in the lignite of Mon-

Capacities in *italics* indicate that 10 per cent has been added to the capacity of the female skull which is the presumed sex from which this particular type is known. Female capacities may generally be approximated by deducting 10 per cent from the male capacity. In the human species the cranial capacity is about 200 cc. more than the volume of the brain.

m = measured with seed; mc = measured and calculated; mw = measured with water; c = calculated; e = estimated.

TABLE IV. AVERAGE CRANIAL CAPACITIES IN ANTHROPOIDS AND MAN. MALES.

Cubic Capacity	Group	Method	Cubic Capacity	Group	Method
97	Gibbon	m	1438	Czechs	m
125	Siamang	m	1439	Fijians and Loyalty Islanders	m
400	Chimpanzee	m	1440	Combe Capelle	e
416	Orang-Utan	m	1442	S. Amer. Indians	c
530	Zinjanthropus boisei	mc	1446	Modern Europeans	c
543	Gorilla	m	1450	Neanderthal	mc
506	Plesianthropus	e	1450	Ingwavuma	e
600	Australopithecus afrícanus	e	1451	Polynesians	m
600	Zinjanthropus boisei	e	1456	Sandwich Islands	m
650	Paranthropus robustus	e	1457	Swanscombe	c
715	Australopithecus prometheus	e	1460	"Kaffirs"	m
723	Homo habilis	mc	1467	Chinese	m
775	Pithecanthropus II	e	1468	Swiss	m
850	Telanthropus	e	1470	Fontéchevade	mc
900	Pithecanthropus robustus	mc	1473	Western Eskimo	m
940	Pithecanthropus I	e	1475	Japanese	m
1000	Paranthropus crassidens	e	1474	Bury St. Edmunds	e
1043	Sinanthropus	mc	1476	Maoris	c
1100	Solo	mc	1480	Ehringsdorf	e
1177	Steinheim	c	1480	Modern English	m
1300	Saccopastore I	c	1487	Tahitian	m
1230	Cape Flats	mw	1490	Buriats	m
1243	Baining	c	1490	Koreans	m
1250	Saldanha	c	1495	E. Centr. Amerinds	c
1256	Australian aborigines N T	c	1498	Kalmucks	m
1264	Tasmanians	c	1500	Springbok Flats	e
1264	Andamanese	m	1501	Ancient Europeans	c
1278	Australian aborigines S A	c	1505	Upper Paleolithic	c
1280	New Guinea	c	1516	Central Eskimo	c
1285	Veddas	m	1519	Iroquois	c
1305	Rhodesian man	mc	1525	Spy I	c
1307	La Quina	c	1530	Chancelade	c
1300	Talgai	c	1532	Algonkin	c
1320	Saccopastore II	c	1532	Matjes River	c
1323	Melanesians	m	1540	Galilee	e
1329	Bushman	mc	1540	Tepexpan	mw
1333	Gibraltar Adult	mc	1550	Monte Circeo	c
1335	Hindu and Tamil	m	1552	Mount Carmel	c
1338	Australian aborigines Victoria	m	1552	Early Neanderthals	mc
1346	African Negroes	m	1552	Classic Neanderthals	mc
1350	American Negroes	mw	1564	Le Moustier	c
1358	Piltdown	e	1573	Mongols	m
1359	Tyrolese	m	1575	Singa	c
1383	Ainu	mc	1590	Predmost	c
1386	London (Lloyds)	e	1593	Keilor	m
1388	Galla and Somali	c	1600	Fish Hoek	c
1400	Galley Hill	m	1600	Teshik-Tash child	e
1403	Dayaks	c	1610	Shanidar I	m
1406	Burmese	m	1625	La Chapelle aux Saints	mc
1408	Hottentots	c	1641	LaFerrassie	mc
1415	Aetas	c	1650	Wadjak	c
1425	Spy II	c	1650	Gibraltar boy	e
1425	Châtelpèrron	mc	1660	Cro-Magnon	c
1424	Malayans	m	1680	Elementeita	c
1427	Marquesans	m	1700	Boskop	e
1434	Moriori	c	1925	Zitzikama	c
1435	1st to 2nd Dynasty Egyptians	c			

QUALITATIVE TRAITS
• Freedom from constraint of biologically predetermined behavioral responses, that is, instincts.
• The potentialities for the development of a complex problem-solving capacity, that is, intelligence.
• The capacity for learning and the retention of learning, that is, educability.
• The capacity for complex symbolic thought.
• Speech as an expression of symbolic thought.
• The development of a complex way of life or culture based on the elaboration of symbols.
• The capacity for innovation.
• Toolmaking.
• Hunting
• Carnivorous or omnivorous diet

Reconstructed Saldanha skull, Saldanha Bay, South Africa.

tebamboli, in the province of Grosseto in Northern Italy. This Lower Pliocene form, dating back some 10 million years, had small teeth, no simian gap, a short face, a steep lower jaw, and a manlike pelvis.

The Proconsulidae and *Oreopithecus* give us some idea of the kind of forms that developed in the line leading to the ancestors of man. They were unspecialized creatures, that is to say, they did not follow any special line of development, but retained a generalized plasticity.

How does a man differ from an ape? This is not an easy question to answer. In any event, in following the evolution of man if we knew all the stages through which that evolution passed—which we do not—we would have to come upon one stage at least in which it would be impossible to say whether the creature with which we are dealing is an ape or a man. There are many similar transitional problems in the field of biology in which, for example, it is difficult to decide whether a certain organism is a plant or an animal or even, as in the case of viruses, whether it is a living thing at all. A phase of evolutionary development between ape and man is easily conceivable in which on morphological grounds one would decide that the creature is an ape, but on functional grounds one would have to agree that it is a man. It must from the outset, therefore, be made clear here that the criteria of humanity are never to be decided upon structural or physical grounds but upon functional or qualitative ones. Although when certain structural stages of development are reached in the primates, as in the upright posture and the large size of the brain, we may be certain that such a creature possessed the functional traits of man. What are these functional or qualitative traits?

The functional or qualitative features which distinguish man from all nonhuman primates are shown in the illustration and chart on page 26.

A man invents, transmits, and perpetuates complexes of symbols which may take the form of ideas, beliefs, religious practices, institutions, domestic articles, tools and the like. Such extracorporeal artifacts are of his making, and they are what ultimately make him and constitute his culture. When we encounter evidences of the existence of any or all of the functions listed in any organism, we may reasonably conclude that we are dealing with a man.

THE EARLIEST MANLIKE FORMS

Zinjanthropus boisei is one of the earliest known men. "Zinj" is the classical Arabic name for East Africa; "anthropus" is the Greek for "man"; "boisei" is the specific name in honor of a benefactor of the expedition, which, under the leadership of Dr. L. S. B. Leakey, discovered *Zinjanthropus* in Olduvai Gorge, Tanganyika Territory, East Africa, in July 1959.

What was discovered was an almost complete skull of a youth of between 16 and 18 years, together with a portion of a shinbone.

27

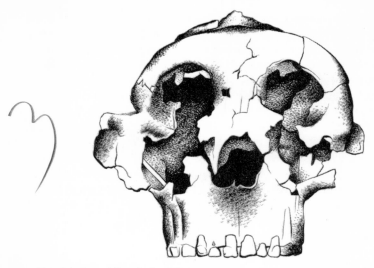

Frontal view of the skull of *Zinjanthropus boisei.*

The cranial capacity was 530 cc. Were one to judge from the form of the skull alone, there would be little hesitation in declaring that this is the skull of an ape, and not of a man. Certainly it is a very manlike ape, but still quite apish, even though there is present a strange medley of apelike and manlike characters in the skull. The face is long and wide; there is a gorillalike sagittal crest on top of the skull to which the temporal muscles were attached; there is almost no brow; the molars and premolars are enormous; however, the canines and incisors are as small or even smaller than they are in contemporary men; and there is not the slightest evidence of a premaxillary diastema. Thus, the skull shows both distinctively apelike and uniquely manlike traits. This is exactly what would be expected in a form transitional between ape and man.

A number of artifacts were found together on the same living floor as the skeletal remains. These were at first attributed to *Zinjanthropus*. These artifacts consisted of stone tools made of quartzite and lava, characterized by having only a few flakes removed in either one or two directions on both faces to make a simple chopping implement with a sharp but irregular cutting edge on either side of the stone. These tools were found on a living floor from which similar tools had been recovered in earlier years.

Because they come from the base of the lowermost bed which had up to that time been excavated, they are known as Olduvai I. Similar tools made from water-worn pebbles have been found in association with three teeth of a manlike form in a cave at Sterkfontein in South Africa. Since no such stone occurs naturally at Olduvai I, the tools found in association with *Zinjanthropus* at that level must have been made from materials which had been brought to the site from elsewhere. The presence of 176 recovered flakes indicates that the tools were manufactured on the spot.

Analysis of the rocks occurring immediately above and below the *Zinjanthropus* site by measuring the potassium 20 and its decay product, argon 40, yielded an age for the *Zinjanthropus* remains of 1,750,000 years. This is more than a million years earlier than had previously been estimated for this specimen.

THE EARLIEST KNOWN HOMININE

Further work on the *Zinjanthropus* site at Olduvai unearthed some cranial fragments together with a lower premolar and an upper molar tooth of a much more manlike form than *Zinjanthropus*. The shinbone and fibula formerly attributed to *Zinjanthropus* may have belonged to this hominine i.e., member of the genus *Homo*.

Though *Zinjanthropus* was doubtless a toolmaker, tools once considered his work are now accredited to this newly discovered man, and *Zinjanthropus*, whose remains were found on the outskirts of the living floor, is now believed to have been an intruder.

Among the Olduvai tools found at the lower part of Bed I, was a bone tool, a "lissoir," probably used for working and polishing skins. Pelts may even have been used for clothing and as mats on which to sleep. Choppers were found with horn and waste flakes, and the metatarsal and metacarpal bones of antelopes, sharpened to a point. These latter tools are striated in a peculiar way, indicating that they were used for digging roots. In assocation were the bones of aquatic birds, catfish, and tortoises— easily caught creatures.

In Bed II at Olduvai, in a site higher up and later than the zinjanthropine, was discovered the remains of the skull of an adolescent of the new form of man. There were fragments of the frontal, parts of both parietals, the greater part of the occipital, parts of both temporal bones, together with a nearly complete lower jaw with all the teeth in place, part of the upper jaw with nearly all the teeth, and part of the lower half of the humerus (upper arm bone).

The cranial capacity of the prezinj child was about 680 cc., possibly 723 cc. This means that in the adult the cranial capacity might have reached 100 to 150 cc. more, bringing the adult capacity up to somewhat more than 800 cc.

The recovered footbones show most of the specializations associated with the erect posture typical of man. The finger bones show the specializations associated with a manlike precision grip—not as well developed as in modern man.

Altogether, the remains of seven individuals of this new form of man were discovered in the Olduvai region, and all these remains are strikingly more manlike than those of any australopithecine. Indeed, they are even more like those of modern man in some respects than those of *Pithecanthropus (Homo) erectus*.

The discovery of a rough circle of loosely piled stones on the living floor in the lower part of Bed I (lower and earlier than the zinjanthropine site), with hundreds of tools all around, in a region in which stones do not naturally occur, indicates that this early hominine built rough shelters or windbreaks.

These facts tell us that we are dealing with a man of the genus *Homo*, a highly skillful man, therefore *habilis*, from the Latin for skillful, *Homo habilis*.

In January 1964 Leakey discovered an almost complete zinjanthropine mandible with all the teeth in place at a new site west of Lake Natron, northeast of Olduvai. This was found in a deposit with fauna of Middle Pleistocene age. The deposit is about 500,000 years later than that from which the original zinjanthropine skull was recovered, and indicates that for this long period the

Oldowan pebble tools (Lava), Bed I, Olduvai Gorge, Tanganyika.

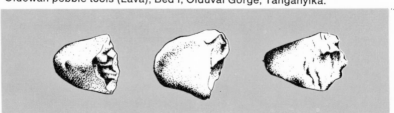

Reconstruction of *Zinjanthropus* manufacturing a tool.

zinjanthropine scarcely underwent any morphological change.

On present evidence, it appears that *Homo habilis* lived before, during, and after the zinjanthropines. It seems, then, that two very different forms of man, one apelike and one much more man-like, were evolving side by side at Olduvai, and probably else-where, during the Upper Villafranchian and during the lower Mid-dle Pleistocene.

Both *Homo habilis* and *Zinjanthropus* lived during a period when many of the animals were passing through a phase of gigan-tism. There were pigs as large as rhinos, sheep that stood seven feet at the shoulder, giant hippos, antelope, cattle, and baboons. But at this stage of his development, *Zinjanthropus* was probably mainly a vegetarian, while *Homo habilis* having extended his diet to meat, was apparently unable to deal with most of these giant forms. He was not yet a hunter of "big" game. He was still the heir of his vegetarian primate ancestors, but had progressed beyond them to the gathering and eating of small animals, as is evidenced by the fact that upon his living floor were found the remains of baby pigs and antelopes, rats, mice, frogs, lizards, snakes, tortoises, and birds.

These animals could be collected with bare hands. The hunting of big game was probably limited to the young animals. *Homo habilis* was clearly much more advanced than *Zinjanthropus*.

Whether the prezinjanthropines or the zinjanthropines were capable of speech it is not possible to say with any degree of certainty, but an animal capable of the degree of abstract thought and symbol usage necessary for the making of stone tools was highly probably capable of speech.

Homo habilis had made the passage from a vegetarian diet to one that included meat-eating, a pivotally important step not only in the cultural but also in the physical evolution of man. Meat requires much less chewing than fibrous plants. Large canine teeth were helpful in shredding the harder coverings of many edible plants, and bony crests were necessary to give attachment to the massive muscles that moved the lower jaw of the plant-eating primate. For the meat-eater, large canine teeth, large jaws, and bony crests are unnecessary. Hence, the changes destined to occur were toward the development of a more manlike head. By reducing the size of the teeth, and hence of the jaws necessary to hold the roots of those teeth, room was afforded for an expanding brain.

That the zinjanthropines probably progressed habitually in an erect position is virtually certain from the fact that their close relatives, the australopithecines of South Africa, had already achieved the erect posture.

The australopithecines flourished in the Lower Pleistocene and probably before, that is, a million or more years ago. They became extinct about 600,000 years ago. The average cranial capacity was less than 600 cc. The australopithecine skull is extremely apelike, and in some forms, such as *Paranthropus crassidens*, which is almost identical with that of *Zinjanthropus boisei*, there is a sagittal crest on top of the skull. In all the australopithecines, the teeth are manlike and generally quite large. However, the form of the pelvis and of the lower extremities is so manlike that there can be no doubt that the australopithecines habitually progressed in the upright posture. From the innumerable examples of the humerus bone of the antelope and bones and jaws with teeth found in association with the broken tops of the skulls of baboons at such australopithecine sites as Makapan, Sterkfontein, and Taung, it is now reasonably certain that the australopithecines were hunters of baboons and possibly other animals. Olduvai I type tools found in the breccia at the back of the Sterkfontein cave in which many australopithecine remains have been found, renders it almost certain that the australopithecines were the makers of these tools and dependent upon them in their hunting and for the carving up of animals. The mainstay of their meat diet appears to have been the baboon, whose easily broken skull made him a favorite target.

The australopithecines, among whom *Zinjanthropus* is to be numbered, are the most primitive known forms of men, and it remains possible that this group may well have been the ancestors of all later forms of man.

THE ENVIRONMENTAL CHANGES LEADING TO THE DEVELOPMENT OF MAN

What were the conditions which led to the appearance of the first men, that is primates who for the first time began to make tools upon which they were dependent for survival?

The principal stimulus which led to the transmutation of an apelike creature into a man was climatic. From the southern tip of South Africa there was a gradual withdrawal of the rainfall toward the equator. As a result, an enormous area of land, which was once fully forested, was turned into steppes or savannas, that is, open plains with relatively few trees and sparse vegetation. This change occurred during the greater part of the Pliocene. In such an environment, manlike apes that had previously lived on an herbivorous diet in the forestlands would, over this long period of secular time, be forced to adapt themselves to an environment very different from that which existed in the forest. In the forest little more was required than to stretch out a hand, grasp some succulent plant, eat, and thus survive. But upon the sparsely vegetated open savanna it was quite another matter, and quite a different response was called for by the new challenges presented by the environment. In the first place, since vegetation was not enough to support life, the early ancestors of man were forced to supplement their diet with meat. At first they continued in their food-gathering habits and extended these to include the gathering of the young and easily secured animals. In order to strip such animals of their hairy and inedible skins, some sharp tool was necessary. A naturally flaked pebble might have provided the model for such a tool, and once the model was available this could then have been artificially

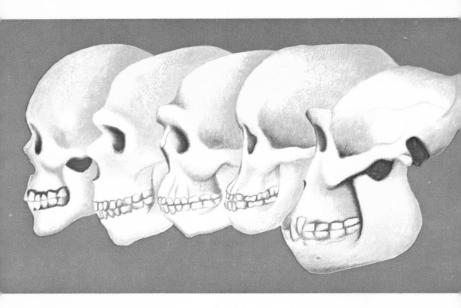

Skulls of gorilla, *Australopithecus, Sinanthropus,* Neanderthal man, and modern man showing progressive changes in various features.

reproduced by flaking similar stones, and in this way the first deliberately manufactured tools would have been produced.

Under such conditions of life the instinctual automatic responses which sufficed apes in their forest environments were not sufficient to meet the requirements of the new surroundings which presented a series of very new challenges. In the savanna locale what was required was not the instinctive automatic reaction, but rather the problem-solving activity leading to the appropriate *response* to novel challenge, that is, intelligence. Those individuals would be favored in the struggle for survival who possessed more of this capacity than those not so well-endowed, and the favored individuals were likely to leave a larger progeny than those not so favored, and thus tend to perpetuate their own kind. In other words, in the savanna environment a premium was placed, by natural selection (see pages 65-68), upon those individuals who exhibited increasingly higher orders of problem-solving activity and fewer and fewer instinctive reactions. It is in this way that man gradually came to lose his instincts and to develop in their place

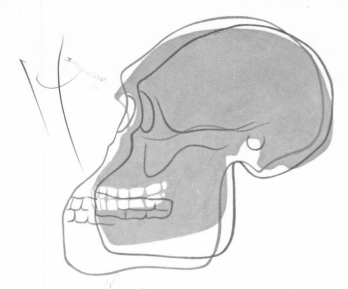

Outlines of skull of *Australopithecus prometheus* (shaded), *Plesianthropus transvaalensis* (brown line), and *Paranthropus robustus* (green line), all oriented in the Frankfurt Plane—from the lowest margins of the orbits to the highest point on the external ear hole.

that trait in which he exceeds all other living creatures, namely, intelligence. Man has none of those psychophysical dispositions causing other animals to perceive stimuli and automatically to react to them.

The loss of instincts and their replacement by potentialities for intelligence necessitated the development of several associated traits. The first of these was an increase in the size of the brain in order to accommodate the increased structural elements required to serve the increasingly complex activities these creatures were called upon to perform. The second was birth in an extremely immature condition, because as a result of the adoption of the erect posture the pelvic outlet was narrowed, while at the same time the brain increased in size, thus making it necessary for the fetus to be born when its head had reached the maximum size compatible with live birth. At birth the average size of the brain is 350 cc. By the end of its first year that brain has more than doubled to 850 cc. The human infant must be born on an average of 267 days after conception. Otherwise it could not be born at all. The human infant is born when only half its gestation is completed; that first half is called the uterogestation period. The second half of its gestation occurs outside the womb, and is therefore called exterogestation. The exterogestation period comes to an end when the infant is able to locomote for itself; that is, when it begins to crawl, which is, on the average, about 267 days after birth. Little marsupials like the opossum or kangaroo have the advantage of spending their exterogestative period in their mother's marsupium or pouch, but the human infant has no such advantage. As a consequence of its physical and physiological immaturity, the dependency of the human infant is extremely prolonged and precarious, and its mother is designed, as a result of the process of natural selection, to meet those needs with all the satisfactions they require.

The third and fourth traits are then, (3) physical immaturity, (4) physiological immaturity, and the fifth trait is (5) behavioral immaturity. Together these traits constitute a sixth, (6) the long period of dependency during which the infant and child is dependent upon others for sustenance and education. Because the child must *learn* from other human beings everything it comes to know and do as a human being in the culture in which it is raised, it must have a long learning period during which it is dependent upon others. They must not only care for its physical but also for its behavioral needs. While other animals adapt themselves to the environment principally by physical means, man's principal mode of adaptation is through *culture*. Thus, man has added an entirely new dimension to the physical and physiological—culture, by far

TABLE V. GROWTH IN BRAIN AND CRANIAL CAPACITY, BOTH SEXES

Age	Weight gm.	Volume cc.	Cranial Capacity cc.
Birth	350	330	350
3 months	526	500	600
6 months	654	600	775
9 months	750	675	925
1 year	825	750	1,000
2 years	1,010	900	1,100
3 years	1,115	960	1,225
4 years	1,180	1,000	1,300
6 years	1,250	1,060	1,350
9 years	1,307	1,100	1,400
12 years	1,338	1,150	1,450
15 years	1,358	1,150	1,450
18 years	1,371	1,175	1,475
20 years	1,378	1,200	1,500

Source: *Growth and Development of the Child*, Part II, 1933, p. 110.

the most important of the three dimensions in which and by which he lives.

The human infant early became and increasingly grew to be more and more dependent upon others for its survival. For this reason women who possessed those traits which enabled them to meet the needs of the dependent infant most proficiently were increasingly naturally selected. This entailed, in addition to the development of the peculiar form of the human breast, the development of those traits of maternal love which are so highly developed in the human female. Selection pressures were all in the direction of women who, by virtue of the fact that they better met the needs of their infants than other women, would leave a larger progeny behind them. Thus maternal love has been at a very high premium in the development of the human species, and this trait has been positively selected both biologically and culturally.

While this trait was being developed in the female, the conditions of life in prehistoric times were such as to place the highest premium upon co-operation among members of the group. Males would frequently hunt as a band. The digging of pits, the making of snares, and the driving of animals in desired directions could all be done better together than apart. The deviant character in such a society was not likely to prosper. It would be the co-operative individuals who would be likely to perpetuate their kind, while the non-co-operative ones were unlikely to do so. The principal responsibility for ministering to the infant's immediate needs falls upon the mother, and the responsibility of providing for them both falls upon the male who is called upon to exhibit many altruistic responses. Such males would increasingly have been selected in the pressures for survival since it would be just such males who would be the more likely to contribute to the survival of their families. And thus the needs of each of the members of the biological family were complemented by their interactive genetic and cultural development.

Teeth grew smaller in adaptation to the enlarging meat diet, and as a response to the increasing use of tools, the canines were reduced in size, the premaxillary diastema subsequently disappeared, and thus the projecting apelike jaws gave rise to a more manlike face, an orthognathic (straight-jawed) rather than prognathic (projecting jawed) face. Reduced jaws and teeth no longer required massive temporal muscles to be attached to a sagittal crest, and

Early hunters.

the reduced stresses and strains transmitted by the excursions of the teeth through the lower jaw rendered unnecessary massive cheekbones and beetle brows (supraorbital tori), for it is these structures that take up and through which such stresses are distributed. As a result of such changes, the skull of contemporary man gradually developed.

The evolution of man may be traced through his cultural and fossil remains, and it is becoming ever more clear that the genetic (physical) and cultural processes of man's development, far from being mutually exclusive, have been interactively operative, and that cultural pressures have exerted a considerable influence upon the genetic and physical evolution of man. Something of these physical and cultural changes may be traced through the artifacts and fossil remains that have been discovered during the last hundred years or so.

The fragments of two lower jaws found in Lower Pleistocene beds at Sangiran in Central Java probably belonged to an early

form of man. The jaw of this form of early man, named *Meganthropus palaeojavanicus*, approaches in thickness that of a gorilla and also that of the australopithecine Swartkrans jaw found at Sterkfontein. *Meganthropus* may well have been ancestral to the pithecanthropines.

The pithecanthropines are represented by a type of fossil man from the Lower and Middle Pleistocene of Java and China. He was in many respects apelike, but clearly a marked advance upon the australopithecines and equally clearly an erect-walking man. *Homo erectus robustus*, formerly called *Pithecanthropus erectus robustus* (the robust erect-walking apeman), from the Lower Pleistocene in the Sangiran district of Java is very robustly built, about 5 feet 6 inches in height. His skull has a low vault and markedly developed brow ridges, with a cranial capacity of about 900 cc. The teeth are larger than in any known form of man, and the canine, though smaller than in the anthropoids, projects beyond the level of the other teeth, and what is quite unique for any form of man, a large premaxillary diastema or simian gap is present on both sides of the upper jaw. These facts show that in the course of man's evolution it was the canine teeth that first underwent reduction, as in the case of *Homo erectus robustus*, and that it was only after this occurred that the premaxillary diastema disappeared. A sagittal crest is present on top of the skull, and the base of the skull is broader than the dome, another unique feature of a hominid skull.

Pithecanthropus erectus of the Middle Pleistocene of Java was the first of the pithecanthropines to be discovered during the years 1890-1897, and represents a more developed form of pithecanthropine than the earlier *robustus*. About half a dozen thigh bones of *erectus* have been found, which, from their completely human form, tell us that he walked perfectly erectly. His cranial capacity varied

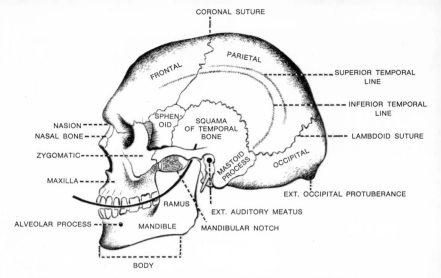

Diagram of human skull. The curved line is the Curve of Spee—a quadrant of a circle passing through the occlusal surface of the teeth and the condyloid process of the mandible.

from 775 to 940 cc., his teeth are all reduced in size, including the canine; the premaxillary diastema is no longer present.

No artifacts were recovered with the Javanese pithecanthropine remains, though many stone artifacts have been found in Java which were almost certainly made by Java man. Artifacts were, however, found together with the fossil remains of pithecanthropines on the Chinese mainland. Peking man or *Sinanthropus pekinensis* (Chinese man from Peking), now more correctly known as *Homo erectus pekinensis*, was discovered at Chou k'ou tien near Peking in a Middle Pleistocene deposit. The fossil remains of over 60 individuals have been found together with artifacts and clear evidence that Peking man made use of fire. Indeed, it is in association with Peking man that we have the first evidence of the use of fire by man. The average cranial capacity of Peking man is 1,043 cc., about 20 per cent greater than Javan man. The frontal region of the skull is rather more globular than in Java man. On the whole, the skull is considerably less robust than in Java man, the teeth are perfectly manlike, and there is no premaxillary diastema.

Peking man is an evolutionary advance upon Java man; nevertheless the two geographic groups are related.

Another early form of man clearly related to the Sino-Malayan pithecanthropines was found on the Solo River near Ngandong in Central Java in an Upper Pleistocene horizon. This was Solo man represented by portions of eleven skulls, from which the faces and teeth were missing. Average cranial capacity was about 1,100 cc., the bones were very thick, as in all other forms of man, and the supraorbital tori well developed. Several beautifully worked bone implements and a number of crude stone tools were found in association with Solo man.

A Pithecanthropine Chellean skull from Olduvai, East Africa

African representatives of the pithecanthropines are known from Olduvai where, in 1960, Leakey discovered the skull, minus the face, of an adult pithecanthropine, and from Algeria, where two pithecanthropine mandibles and teeth, together with associated artifacts of Chello-Acheulian industry, were found in a Middle Pleistocene deposit. More fragmentary remains were found at Sidi Abderrahman (with an associated Middle Acheulian industry) at Rabat, near Casablanca, in Morocco, in Middle Pleistocene deposits. These are almost certainly pithecanthropine. A possible pithecanthropine may be represented by the badly crushed and weathered fragments of three skulls of Upper Pleistocene age found at Lake Eyasi in Tanganyika Territory. The associated stone artifacts were of early Levalloisian industry. The exact status of Lake Eyasi man (*Africanthropus njarasensis* as he was first named) remains uncertain.

A very early neanderthaloid link with the pithecanthropines was found in 1958 at Ma-Pa in Northern Kwangtung, China. This is represented by the greater part of a skull cap of a middle-aged

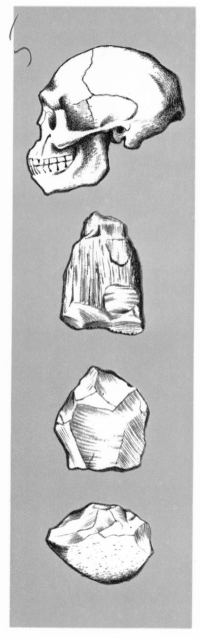

Skull of Solo man, with unassociated artifacts of Soan culture group.

male with the right orbit and greater part of the nasal bones. The skull bears close resemblance to the pithecanthropines in some features, and in others to the neanderthaloids, but is clearly more neanderthaloid than pithecanthropine. The supraorbital torus very much resembles that of *Homo erectus pekinensis*, but is thickest toward the nasal side as in neanderthaloids, and is unlike the condition in the pithecanthropines in which the torus is thicker laterally. Its age has not yet been determined.

Heidelberg man is represented by a complete lower jaw found in

Reconstruction of Chinese Pithecanthropines *(Sinanthropus pekinensis)*.

a Lower Pleistocene deposit at Mauer, in Germany, near Heidelberg. There were no associated artifacts. The jaw is quite massive with a very broad ramus; no chin; a shallow sigmoid notch; but teeth like those of modern man, except that they are a little more "swollen."

A fragment of the ramus of a mandible found at an early Upper Pleistocene level at Saldanha, in South Africa, matches the Mauer jaw perfectly. The skull cap of Saldanha man, associated with primitive stone axes and other implements, is almost identical in form with the skull of Rhodesian man found in a cave at Broken Hill in Rhodesia at an Upper Pleistocene level associated with African Middle Stone Age implements. Cranial capacity of Rhodesian man was 1,250 cc. These skulls combine pithecanthropine and neanthropic (new man, that is, modern type) traits. The face and palate are large in all dimensions, the upper jaw projects, and the overhanging brow ridges are markedly well developed.

The combination of neanderthaloid and neanthropic features revealed by these Rhodesian men are of the greatest interest be-

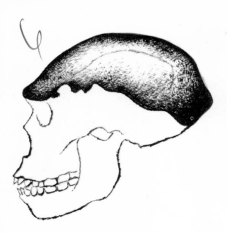

Pithecanthropus erectus I.

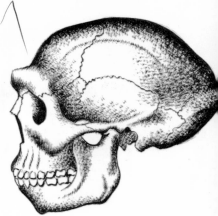

Sinanthropus pekinensis.

cause they clearly represent a form transitional between the pithecanthropines on the one hand and neanderthaloids and modern man on the other.

The earliest type of neanderthaloid thus far discovered in Europe is Steinheim man, found at Steinheim-am-Murr in Germany, represented by a somewhat crushed probably female skull, with artifacts of Acheulian industry, in a Middle Pleistocene deposit of the Mindel-Riss interglacial period. The skull exhibits a curious blend of Neanderthal and neanthropic traits. The occiput (back part) and the face display some neanthropic traits, though the forehead region is characterized by well-developed brow ridges. Cranial capacity was 1,070 cc., rather small for a female neanderthaloid (in whom the average cranial capacity is 1,330 cc.). Steinheim man may well be a descendant of Heidelberg man.

Sinanthropus jaw.

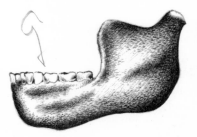

Heidelberg jaw.

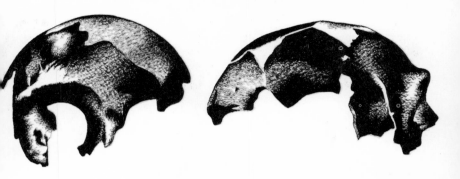

Frontal and right lateral views of Ma-Pa skull.

A fossil representative of man intermediate between Heidelberg and Neanderthal man is known from a lower jaw with undeveloped chin from the Middle Pleistocene of Montmaurin in the Haute-Garonne in France. This was associated with a stone industry preceding the Mousterian industry, named after Le Moustier in France where tools associated with Neanderthal man were first discovered.

Neanderthal man, perhaps the best known and the most misrepresented of our fossil relations, is known from the fossil remains of well over a hundred individuals from Asia and Europe. Neanderthal man is essentially an Upper Pleistocene form, who, because of his heavy brow ridges, undeveloped chin and principally as a result of prejudices or preconceived notions as to what "primitive man" should look like, has been foisted upon an unsuspecting

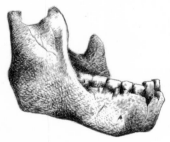

Atlanthropus jaw.

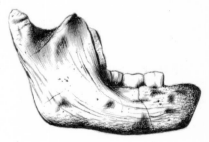

Montmaurin jaw.

45

world as a bestial caricature of a cross between a gorilla and a man! A club-wielding monster with a bull-neck, knock-knees, who walked with a stoop, and assisted his womenfolk on their perambulations with him by dragging them along by their hair! This libel upon Neanderthal man should not be perpetuated because it is untrue. It is of interest only because it illustrates how badly the prejudices of so-called authorities can distort the facts.

The facts about Neanderthal man are the following: he walked perfectly erectly, did not have a bull-neck, had well-developed supraorbital ridges, an undeveloped chin, and an average cranial capacity of 1,550 cc., a larger brain, on the average, by about 150 cc. or more than modern white man! He was the maker of tools of beautiful manufacture known as Mousterian, and was the first man known to bury his dead, to prepare their bodies with red ochre, and send them into the other world accompanied by artifacts and food. It is thus certain that Neanderthal man had a highly developed cultural and spiritual life.

Neanderthal domestic scene.

Many neanderthaloid skulls, like those of the woman of Ehrings-dorf, Spy II, Galilee, and Gibraltar II display some distinctively neanthropic traits. That there may have been some admixture between neanderthaloid and neanthropic types is suggested by the findings, made in 1931-1932, in the caves on the slopes of Mount Carmel in Palestine. Here was found a frankly Neanderthal type, the Tabūn group, and another closely approaching neanthropic man, the Skhūl group. At first believed to be of about the same antiquity, recent dating methods indicate that the more advanced Skhūl group flourished some 10,000 years after the Tabūn group. It is, however, quite possible that some of the ancestors of the Tabūn group had hybridized with a neanthropic type of man to produce the Skhūl type. Ten thousand years is a very short time in the evolutionary time scale, and it is highly improbable that the genetic changes (mutations) necessary to change a Tabūn Neanderthal into a neanthropic type like Skhūl could have occurred over so short a period of time. On the other hand, it is quite possible that the ancestors of these two types of men never met and belonged to two independent populations.

That a neanthropic type of man existed contemporaneously with and may even have antedated some forms of Neanderthal man is indicated by two very interesting finds.

The Swanscombe skull, found in a quarry in the town of that name in Kent, England, in 1935-1936, and partly in 1953, is known from two parietal bones and an occipital bone. The associated culture was Middle Acheulian. Except for the thickness of the bones, which may be matched by some modern skulls, the skull is in every way neanthropic. Unfortunately, the absence of the frontal bone does not enable us to say with certainty that the bone would have been of neanthropic form.

Portions of two other skulls, found at Fontéchevade in central France, associated with a Tayaçian culture, a pre-Mousterian, that is, pre-Neanderthal, culture, are almost certainly of neanthropic type. Fontéchevade I is represented by the forehead region just over the root of the nose including a small portion of the left supraorbital margin. There is not the slightest suggestion of a supra-

Steinheim skull.

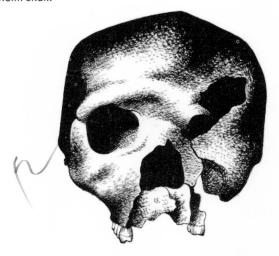

orbital torus, and, indeed, the bone is so gracile that it is either that of a female or an older adolescent neanthropic type. Fontéchevade II is represented by a skullcap with the base, the occiput, and supraorbital portions missing. There is nothing in the structure of this skull to suggest that it is not of a neanthropic type of man. It is very unlikely to have been characterized by supraorbital tori, of which there are not the least evidences.

There are suggestions of the contemporaneous existence of neanthropic and Neanderthal man in Yugoslavia in the form of several juvenile skulls and one adult skull from a cave at Veternica and of a skull cap of a child from Krapina. At Kanjera, in Kenya, in what has been described as a Middle or Late Pleistocene deposit, associated with Acheulian artifacts, there have been discovered the fragmentary skeletal remains of three individuals of Negroid type. Uranium tests show that the Kanjera men lived at the same time as the extinct associated fauna. Nevertheless, the deposit in which this assemblage was found may be of Upper Pleistocene age.

In any event, it is clear that by the Upper Pleistocene, types of modern man, *Homo sapiens*, had already differentiated into populations that had evolved a variety of different adaptive traits of an hereditary nature. Such populations are usually called "races," but

Neanderthal skull.

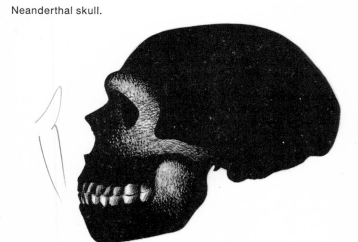

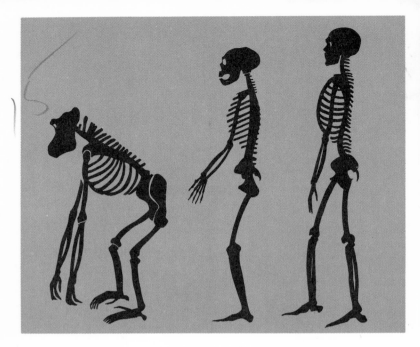

Showing the prejudiced and incorrect version of the Neanderthal skeleton (center) compared with gorilla and modern man's skeleton.

owing to the confusions of thought with which that term is generally invested, it is better to use some other term, such as *ethnic group*, which leaves the question open as to precisely what the population is and how it differs from others. The term *genogroup* may also be used, meaning a breeding population that differs from others in one or more genes.

Types of Upper Pleistocene neanthropic man *(Homo sapiens)* are represented by Châtelperron man, from the cave of La Grotte des Fées, Châtelperron, in central France, represented by a massive skull cap, and associated with Châtelperronian artifacts. The skull is very broad, has thick bones, and a cranial capacity of about 1,425 cc. or more.

Cro-Magnon man, from the village of that name in south-central France and also known from the Red Rocks of the Côte d'Azur on the French Riviera, and from Paviland Cave in southwestern Wales, had a very large braincase and small face; some individuals reached a height of 5 feet 11 inches, and had a cranial capacity of

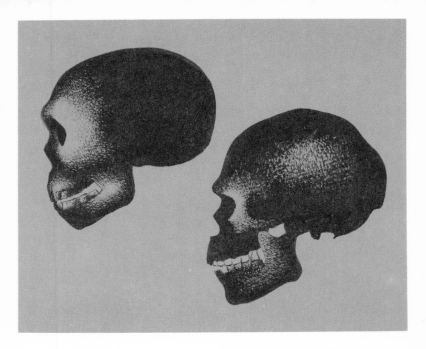

Tabūn (left) and Skhūl (right) skulls.

1,660 cc. They were the makers of those beautiful artifacts which are typically associated with the Aurignacian period, and they are believed to have been the artists responsible for the cave paintings and sculptures which have been discovered in many parts of Europe.

Grimaldi man was discovered in the Grotte des Enfants, below the village of Grimaldi on the Côte d'Azur, where the skeletal remains of a female of about 30 years and of a boy of about 15 years were found in association with artifacts of Aurignacian culture. Immediately above these remains, at various levels up to the floor level of the cave, were found the remains of four Crô-Magnons.

Cranial capacity of the female is 1,265 cc. and of the boy, 1,454 cc. The teeth of the Grimaldis are larger, the upper and lower jaws more projecting, and the chin rather more receding than in the Crô-Magnons. These traits suggest a possible Negroid ancestry for the Grimaldis.

Possible hybridization (see page 70) between Neanderthal and

51

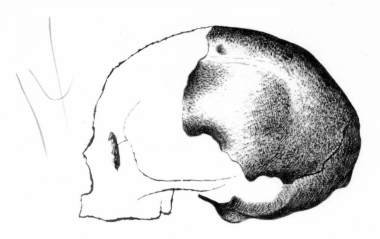

Reconstruction of Swanscombe skull.

Crô-Magnon is suggested by the skeletal finds made at Předmost in Czechoslovakia, associated with a late Aurignacian or early Solutrean culture. Skeletal remains of over 40 individuals were found and these exhibit a medley of Neanderthal and neanthropic traits. The mean cranial capacity is 1,590 cc. In the development of the supraorbital ridges, the length of the skull in front of the ear, and in the retention of some degree of prognathism, the neanderthaloid ancestry of Předmost man is believed to be reflected. Another possible population descended from a cross between a Neanderthal and a neanthropic type is Afalou man from Afalou bou Rummel in North Africa. Recovered from a rock shelter site of Upper Pleistocene age, there were some 50 skeletons associated with implements of Oranian (Capsian) culture, closely related to the Aurignacian of Europe.

Asselar man is represented by an Upper Pleistocene fossil skeleton, undoubtedly Negroid, from Asselar in the central Sahara Desert. The skeleton closely resembles the Nilotic Negro of today. Evidence of this kind makes it clear that the Negroid types of Africa were already differentiated by the Upper Pleistocene.

Early differentiation of ethnic groups is indicated by the find in the Upper Cave at Chou k'ou tien of ten skeletons which yielded three well-preserved skulls of upper paleolithic age. One skull of an old man could pass for that of an archaic European. The second skull, that of a middle-aged woman, could pass for an Eskimo, and

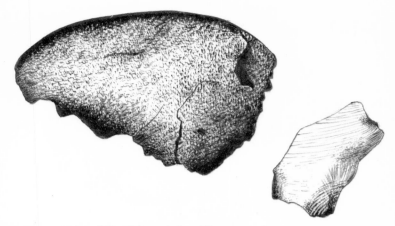

Cranial remains of Fontéchevade I and II.

the third skull, that of a young woman, resembles that of a Melanesian. Considering that these individuals were probably members of the same family, this diversity of physical type is surprising and may well represent another example of hybridization in process.

The land masses of the Old and New Worlds are at one place separated from each other by a distance of little more than 50 miles (the distance between Siberia and Alaska), by the Bering

TABLE VI. CRANIAL CAPACITIES OF NEANDERTHAL MAN IN CUBIC CENTIMETERS

Early			Later	
EUROPE			EUROPE	
Ehringsdorf ♀		1,480	Gibraltar boy* ♂	1,650
Saccopastore ♀		1,200	La Ferrassie ♂	1,641
Krapina		?	La Chapelle-aux-Saints ♂	1,625
			Le Moustier ♂	1,564
SOUTHWEST ASIA			Monte Circeo ♂	1,550
Mt. Carmel, Skhul 4 ♂		1,550	Spy I ♂	1,525
Mt. Carmel, Skhul 5 ♂		1,520	Neanderthal ♂	1,450
Mt. Carmel, Skhul 9 ♂		1,590	Spy II ♂	1,425
Mt. Carmel, Skhul 2 ♀		1,300	La Naulette	?
Mt. Carmel, Tabun 1 ♀		1,270	Engis	?
Galilee, Israel ♀		1,400	Gibraltar ♀	1,333
Shukbah, Israel		?	La Quina ♀	1,307
Shanidar, Kurdistan ♂		1,610		
Bisitum, Iran		?		
Average Male		*1,568*	*Average Male*	*1,553*
Average Female		*1,330*	*Average Female*	*1,320*

*Six-year-old with capacity of 1,400 cc., corrected to probable adult capacity.

Map showing distribution
of localities in which
remains of Neanderthal man
have been found.

TYPES AND DISTRIBUTION OF NEANDERTHAL MAN

The designation "Neanderthal man" actually refers to a variety of man who, far from being the homogeneous "type" he is generally represented as, consists of a variety of forms which are morphologically distinguishable as (1) Early Neanderthals, and (2) Later Neanderthals.

The Early Neanderthals are associated with the Third or Riss-Würm Interglacial, and are represented by such specimens as Ehringsdorf, Saccopastore, Krapina, Mount Carmel, Galilee, Teshik-Tash. The *Later Neanderthals,* associated with the Fourth Glacial or Würm I, are represented by such forms as Gibraltar, La Ferrassie, La Chapelle-aux-Saints, Le Moustier, Monte Circeo, Spy I and II, Neanderthal, La Naulette, Engis, La Quina, La Chaise, Shanidar.

Early Neanderthals. The Third Interglacial (Riss-Würm) Neanderthals differ from the Later Neanderthals in the following features of cranial morphology: The skull is slightly shorter, narrower, and higher, the supraorbital tori are slightly heavier, the parietals and occipital are slightly more expanded, the vault more arched, the cranial base more flexed, the external auditory meatus tends to be vertically elliptical rather than horizontally so, the tympanic plate tends to be vertically or obliquely oriented, the facial skeleton tends to be smaller, there is a tendency to separation of ciliary and orbital portions of the supraorbital torus, the malar is large with sharp demarcation between it and the maxilla, and there is a tendency to formation of a canine fossa. In most of these traits the Early Neanderthals more closely resemble modern man than do the Later Neanderthals.

Later Neanderthals. The Fourth Glacial (Würm) Neanderthal's principal area of distribution was Southwestern Europe. Sites which have yielded Later Neanderthal remains are, *Germany:* Neanderthal, *Belgium:* Bay-Bonnet, Engis, La Naulette, Spy, *Channel Islands:* St. Brelade, Jersey, *France:* Malarnaud (Ariège), La Chaise, La Quina, Petit-Puymoyen (Charente), La Chapelle-aux-Saints (Correze), Genay (Côte d'Or), Combe Grenal, La Ferrassie, Le Moustier, Pech de l'Azé (Dordogne), Monsempron (Lot-et-Garonne), Hyena and Wolf Caves, Arcy-sur-Cure (Yonne), *Spain:* Bañolas, Cova Negra, Gibraltar (Forbes Quarry), Devil's Tower, Piñar, *Italy:* Fosselone and Guattarí Caves (Monte Circeo), Santa Croce di Bisceglie.

The Later Neanderthals differ from the Early Neanderthals in the following cranial features: Larger, lower, and wider cranial vault, with frequent postlambdoidal flattening (resulting from peculiar pattern of growth and closure of lambdoid suture), less flexed cranial base, more sharply angulated occipital bone with relatively heavier occipital tori, more horizontal orientation of tympanic plate, with heavier anterior and posterior portions, larger facial skeleton, large round orbits, large nasal aperture, large interorbital spaces, semicircular supraorbital tori with fused medial and lateral elements, with no concavity of maxilla from body to malar, there is a convergence of maxillary walls and absence of the canine fossa.

The Later Neanderthals were robustly built and of fairly short stature (about 1.65 m. 5 feet 5 inches).

As will be seen from Table VI (p. 53) there appears to have been no difference in the size of the brain between Early and Later Neanderthal man.

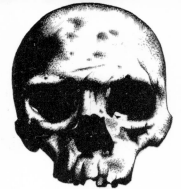

Protomongoloid

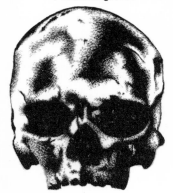

Melanesoid

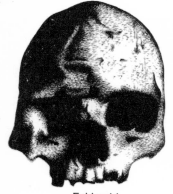

Eskimoid

Straits, with the Big and Little Diomede Islands in between. The Straits are easily navigable by boat, and in winter it is possible to walk across the Straits on the ice. In March 1913 Captain Max Gottschalk did so with his sled and 16 dogs. Authorities generally agree that it was by this route that man, in the prehistoric period, entered North America from Asia. Precisely when this first occurred is not known. Though it may have been considerably earlier than the safest figure, which at the present time is about 25,000 years ago. A portion of a human pelvis found at Natchez in 1845 has been dated by the fluorine method as contemporary with the ground sloth (*Mylodon harlani*), and since the latter became extinct at least 11,000 years ago, we know that man must have entered the Americas before then.

Midland Man, a fragmented skull and some teeth, found at Midland in west-central Texas in 1953, is on the basis of cross-checked radiocarbon dated between 10,000 and 20,000 years old.

Artifacts without skeletal remains found in Sandia Cave, New Mexico, are believed to be about 25,000 years old.

Thought to be of one family, these skulls from the upper cave of Chou k'ou tien, show the same notable variability exhibited by Upper Paleolithic peoples.

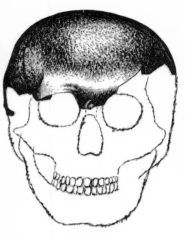

Châtelperron skull.

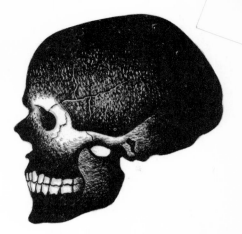

Crô-Magnon skull.

In South America, the oldest evidences of man, both skeletal and associated artifacts, from the Palli Aike Cave in Patagonia, have been dated by the radiocarbon method to be 8,639±450 years old.

Until further evidence is forthcoming, our present knowledge puts the entry of man into the Americas as not much earlier than 25,000 years ago.

THE FACTORS OF HOMINID EVOLUTION

The factors or processes that have been operative in the evolution of man have been:

Culture

Natural Selection

Mutation

Isolation

Genetic Drift

Hybridization

Sexual Selection

Social Selection

Culture is the class of things or events, dependent upon the symbolic process, considered in an extrabodily context, that is, in their relationships to one another, rather than in terms of their relationships to the human organism. In the latter context such acts, dependent upon symboling, constitute *human behavior*. Things and events dependent upon symboling are called *symbolates*. Symbolates are such things as ideas, attitudes, beliefs, sentiments, acts,

Mackenzie Area: 1. Kutchin; **2.** Ingalik; **3.** Tanana; **4.** Tanaina; **5.** Han; **6.** Dog Rib; **7.** Yellow Knife; **8.** Tahltan; **9.** Slave; **10.** Sekani; **11.** Beaver; **12.** Chipewayan; **13.** Tsimshian; **14.** Sarsi; **15.** Carrier

Northwest Coast: 1. Tlingit; **2.** Tsimshian; **3.** Haida; **4.** Kwakiutl; **5.** Nootka; **6.** Coast; **7.** Salish; **8.** Chinook; **9.** Takelma; **10.** Hupa; **11.** Yurok **12.** Aleut

Plateau: 1. Thompson; **2.** Okanagan; **3.** Flathead; **4.** Nez Perce; **5.** Bannock; **6.** Snake; **7.** Klamath

Southwestern: 1. Navaho; **2.** Hopi; **3.** Tewa; **4.** Keresan; **5.** Zuñi; **6.** Havasupai; **7.** Mohave; **8.** Yuma; **9.** Pima; **10.** W. Apache; **11.** Mescalero; **12.** Seri; **13.** Papago; **14.** Tarahumara; **15.** Yaqui; **16.** Mayo

California Basin: 1. Klamath; **2.** Modoc; **3.** N. Shoshoni; **4.** Paviotso; **5.** Shoshoni; **6.** Karok; **7.** Miwok; **8.** Pomo; **9.** Mono; **10.** Yokuts; **11.** Salinan; **12.** Southern Paiute; **13.** Ute; **14.** Mohave

The Plains: 1. Blackfoot; **2.** Assiniboine; **3.** Gros Ventre; **4.** Flathead; **5.** Crow; **6.** Bannock; **7.** Mandan; **8.** Hidatsa; **9.** Arikara; **10.** Dakota; **11.** Ponca; **12.** Omaha; **13.** Osage; **14.** N. Shoshoni; **15.** Arapaho; **16.** Cheyenne; **17.** Kiowa; **18.** Wichita; **19.** Comanche; **20.** Mescalero; **21.** Caddo; **22.** Tonkawa; **23.** Lipan

Northeastern: 1. Naskapi; **2.** Cree; **3.** Montagnais; **4.** Beothok; **5.** Assiniboine; **6.** Ojibwa; **7.** Ottawa; **8.** Dakota; **9.** Fox; **10.** Sauk; **11.** Menomini; **12.** Winnebago; **13.** Kickapoo; **14.** Iowa; **15.** Illinois; **16.** Miami; **17.** Algonquin; **18.** Huron; **19.** Iroquois; **20.** Erie; **21.** Micmac; **22.** Abenaki; **23.** Penobscot; **24.** Massachusetts; **25.** Lenape; **26.** Powhatan

Southeastern: 1. Shawnee; **2.** Cherokee; **3.** Yuchi; **4.** Chickasaw; **5.** Creek; **6.** Lipan; **7.** Tonkawa; **8.** Natchez; **9.** Choctaw; **10.** Seminole; **11.** Timucua

Mexican: 1. Tepehuane; **2.** Huichol; **3.** Cora; **4.** Otomi; **5.** Aztec; **6.** Tarascan; **7.** Zapotecan; **8.** Maya

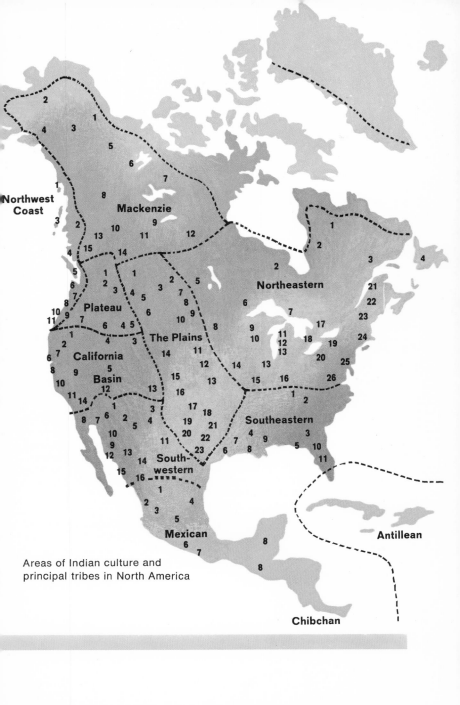

Areas of Indian culture and
principal tribes in North America

METHODS OF DATING

Radiocarbon Dating. The radiocarbon method of dating organic materials was worked out and developed by Professor W. F. Libby at the Institute of Nuclear Physics at the University of Chicago. It was originally not possible to obtain reliable dates by this method beyond 30,000 years, but by a recent refinement of this method it is possible to compute the age of any organic material up to about 70,000 years. This new investigational tool has been particularly useful in the dating of American Indian remains. The method is based on the fact that radioactive carbon (Carbon 14), which is liberated in the atmosphere as a result of the interaction of cosmic rays with nitrogen, is present in all living structures. During the life of the organism an equilibrated and constant percentage of C^{14} is maintained in its carbon structure. This percentage is believed to be the same for every form of life. With death the supply of carbon and C^{14} to the organism abruptly ceases, and the C^{14} atoms begin to disintegrate. It is believed that not only is the concentration of C^{14} the same in all living organisms, but that the rate of C^{14} disintegration after death is also the same. Therefore, if the rate of disintegration of C^{14} can be established for a sample of known age, it becomes possible to check the accuracy of this method of dating. This has been done with considerable success. It has been shown that after 5760 ± 30 years have elapsed one half of the C^{14} atoms have disintegrated. Where formerly some six grams of carbon had to be extracted from specimens before its age could be determined, newer methods have reduced this to about half a gram.

By a most ingenious method the Dutch investigators, Drs. A. Haring and H. de Vries, of Amsterdam and Groningen respectively, have made it possible to determine the age of organic remains up to a period of about 70,000 years. This is done by the method of isotopic enrichment. The CO_2 obtained from the original material is reduced to CO by leading it over zinc at a temperature of $380° \pm 5°$ C. The CO is enriched in five thermal diffusion columns connected in parallel, each column having a length of 430 cm. The enrichment is derived from the abundance of O^{18} in the CO. For the activity measurements the enriched CO is oxidized again by leading it over CuO. Enrichment by a factor of 16 takes about two months, and this enrichment shifts the limit of counting to upwards of 70,000 years.

The Uranium Radiometric Dating Method. A new method for the relative dating of bones and teeth is by radiometric assay of the uranium they may contain. When bones are buried in deposits through which water containing uranium circulates, the calcium atoms in the hydroxyapatite are replaced by those of uranium. The longer the bone is buried the greater the amount of uranium accumulated. The radioactivity of the adsorbed uranium, in the form of the rate of its beta radiations, can be measured since the enamel of a tooth is considerably less absorptive than its dentine, and will therefore be considerably less radioactive, and since fossils from limestone formations and clay accumulate less uranium than those from gravels and sands of the same age, the results obtained must be interpreted with caution, as is the case with the method of fluorine analysis. The advantage of the uranium method over the fluorine method is that it does not involve the destruction of the material tested.

The Nitrogen Dating Method. In fresh or recently buried bones the nitrogen content is high, about 4 per cent. With the passage of time, as fluorine increases, nitrogen decreases. Hence, determination of the organic nitrogen content of bones will yield some idea of their relative age. This, in a recent (1958) re-determination of the fluorine and nitrogen contents of the bones from several famous sites Oakley obtained the following results:

	Fluorine Per cent	Nitrogen Per cent
Modern bones	0.01	4.0
Neolithic skull	0.3	1.9
Galley Hill skeleton	0.5	1.6
Swanscombe skull	1.7	nil
Fossil mammal bones, Swanscombe gravel	> 1.5	traces

The Potassium-Argon Dating Method. This method is still in process of development, but may prove of great importance in the future. Age of organic materials is determined by the ratio of potassium 40 to argon 40 they contain. Potassium 40, a radioactive form of the element, is present in all living things. It decays into argon 40 at the rate of 50 per cent every 1.3/10 billion years. By determining the amount of potassium 40 that has decayed into argon 40, the passage of time since the specimen had been part of a living system can be determined, since potassium is incorporated into tissues only during life.

A difficulty of the method is that mineral deposits much older than the specimen may have contaminated it, and thus render the age determination dubious. This, however, is a difficulty which need not apply in many cases, and in those in which it does could, possibly, be overcome.

Thermoluminescence. The essence of this method, based on the fact that all sorts of materials are to some extent radioactive, is the heating of the material, pottery, lava, and the like, to the point below which it gives off light itself. This releases thermoluminescence, which is caused by electrons being freed from the soils in which they have been trapped for many years.

Over the years the radioactivity contained in all materials decays, giving off alpha and beta particles which trap electrons in solid crystals. The older the material, the more electrons are trapped.

When the material is heated up to about 350 degrees centigrade or less, the electrons are returned and create a mild light that can be captured by a photomultiplier tube. The more light the older the material.

The method is good for about 100,000 years.

Illustrating ecological rules: Nilotic Negroes with elongated body and extremities, and melanin pigmentation.

ECOLOGICAL RULES

Allen's Rule states that in warmblooded animals the relative size of protruding body parts, ears, snouts, noses, necks, limbs, and tails, decreases with decrease in temperature. These protruding parts are shorter among those populations of the species living in the cooler parts of the species range. In man, for example, the limbs of Eskimos are shorter than in African Negroes.

Bergmann's Rule states that within a warmblooded species the body-size of populations of the species usually increases with decreasing mean temperature of its habitat. Body-weight is also correlated with mean temperature. High body weights tend to be associated with low temperatures, low body weights with high temperatures, and medium body weights with temperate regions. The selective advantage of such body-weight relations to temperature may be deduced from the fact that for a given stature lower body-weight at higher temperatures yields an advantageous ratio of body surface area to mass, thereby facilitating the maintenance of body heat in a cold environment. Since larger bodied individuals have a smaller surface

Eskimos: heavy-boned, medium-to-short in stature; long trunks, short legs, small-to-average hands, large faces, broad jaws, and light pigmentation.

in proportion to mass—volume and mass increasing as the cube of the linear dimensions and surface only as the square—a larger body size serves to reduce heat radiation, and a smaller body size to increase it. In man, for example, the taller linear peoples tend to live in high temperature regions, such as many Africans, while those with rather thickset body builds, like the Eskimo, tend to live in below-freezing temperatures.

Gloger's Rule states that melanin pigmentation tends to increase in the warm and humid parts of the species range. High humidity together with high temperature promotes the formation of black pigmentation (eumelanins), while aridity with high temperature promotes the formation of the reddish, yellowish- and reddish-brown pigments (phaeomelanins). The phaeomelanins tend to be reduced under cooler conditions even if arid, as do the melanins under extreme cases such as the polar regions. The maximum depth of pigmentation is found in humid and hot climates, the minimum in arctic climates. Heat and aridity, as in subtropical deserts, tend to promote yellowish- and reddish-browns, while lower temperature and aridity, as in steppes, tends to promote greys and grey-browns.

patterns of behavior, customs, codes, institutions, works and forms of art, languages, tools, implements, machines, utensils, ornaments, fetishes, charms, and the like. Thus, culture, as distinct from human behavior, acquires a life of its own and is not only enlarged and transmitted from generation to generation, but works upon and molds human beings according to the forms, patterns, and pressures it exhibits. The cultural contributions that men make during their lifetime live on long after their bodies have decayed, and long after they have ceased to be capable of corporeal behavior, though their physical creations, their tools, spears, pots, paintings, and other objects may be regarded as congealed forms of human behavior. But such creations regarded in their interrelationships among themselves, and not in relation to the organism, are cultural artifacts. Human behavior is somatic; culture is extrasomatic. One cannot transmit human behavior as an entity in itself, but one can transmit the symbols which when taught to the human being will enable him to behave according to the cultural pattern in which he has been conditioned.

From the earliest stages of man's evolution culture has increasingly been man's principal means of adapting himself to the environment. Culture is an agency not only for controlling, but for changing the pressures of natural selection, and thus for influencing the evolution of man both physically and culturally. The cultural processes through which such evolutionary changes have been achieved are the development of tools, marriage regulations, social selection, co-operativeness, economic development, migration, improved care of children, and the like. Cultural pressures have been principally responsible for changing primate nature into human nature, among other means by replacing instinct with intelligence. By this means man escaped from the bondage of body instincts to the freedom of the extrasomatic world of ideas and symbols which he could endow with a meaning, a shape, and a form, and which he, in turn, could cause to serve his purposes in making himself more comfortable in the world.

The invention and development of tools almost certainly played a part in the subsequent reduction in the size of the teeth and in the projection of the jaws, as well as in the adoption of the fully erect posture. Implements like the spear and the bow and arrow may well have exercised a selective effect upon body build. The action of culture upon the evolution of man has already been dis-

Magdalenian sculpture. Horse's head on antler, Mas d'Azil (Ariège).

cussed on pages 34-38 and will be again discussed under Social Selection and Sexual Selection.

Natural selection is the major process by means of which progressive development is brought about in living organisms. It was originally, and is still, best defined by Charles Darwin in the following words: "As many more individuals of each species are born than can possibly survive; and as, consequently, there is a frequently recurring struggle for existence, it follows that any being, if it vary however slightly in any manner profitable to life itself, under the complex and sometimes varying conditions of life, will have a better chance of surviving, and thus be *naturally selected*. From the strong principle of inheritance, any selected variety will tend to propagate its new and modified form." (*The Origin of Species*, 1859, p. 5.) The short statement of this principle is "differential fertility," that is, those who have the necessary adaptive fitness are more likely to leave a larger progeny behind them than those who don't.

While it is highly probable that almost all man's physical traits, as well as many functional traits, are the result of natural selection, the complexity of the mechanisms involved is frequently so great that it will take many years of research before the adaptive value of even a few human traits will be understood. An exception is skin color. A darkly pigmented skin is an advantage in regions of high sunlight intensity and under conditions of prolonged exposure to solar radiation. Skin cancer in India, for example, is almost exclusively confined to Europeans, and cancer of the skin is comparatively frequent among whites and rare among non-whites.

65

Even here we do not know the whole story. We need more research in order to find out. Nor do we know enough about the adaptive value (if any) of the different hair forms and nose shapes. There are, however, some features of the human body which do correlate well with the environments in which they occur, so that it is not difficult to evaluate their adaptive value. For example, populations living in regions of extreme cold, such as those of the Arctic Circle, Siberia, Alaska, and Greenland, tend to be

THE CLASSIFICATION OF THE HOMINIDAE

A brief classification of the Hominidae is set out below. This may be used as an alternative to that which has been used in the following pages, or simply as a mnemonic. This brief classification may serve to suggest relationships and also to raise further questions. Some of these may be mentioned here.

Firstly, the admission of *Oreopithecus* to hominid status is still *sub judice,* therefore until the full evidence becomes available the ascription to hominid status remains tentative.

Secondly, the recognition of four genera of australopithecines remains open to some doubt. *Plesianthropus* should rank as a species of *Australopithecus,* and so should *Paranthropus* and *Zinjanthropus.*

Thirdly, some workers would be inclined to classify Neanderthal man as a member of the species *erectus.* There is no insuperable objection to such a procedure. It would, in fact, be perfectly legitimate. It should, however, be recognized that the neanderthaloids and neanthropic forms of man were almost certainly not reproductively isolated, and that therefore any specific differences between them must be based on morphological considerations. The suggestion here is that the large size of the brain of the neanderthaloids far outweighs other morphological differences in bringing the neanderthaloids into the species *sapiens* as a subspecies *neanderthalensis.* On this procedure there may be differences of opinion.

FAMILY HOMINIDAE		TABLE VII.
Subfamily Oreopithecinae	**Subfamily Australopithecinae**	**Subfamily Homininae**
Genus *Oreopithecus*	Genus *Australopithecus*	Genus *Homo*
Species *bambolii*	Species *africanus*	Species *erectus*
	Species *prometheus*	Subspecies *erectus*
	Genus *Paranthropus*	Subspecies *robustus*
	Species *crassidens*	Subspecies *pekinensis*
	Species *robustus*	Subspecies *soloensis*
	Genus *Plesianthropus*	Subspecies *mauritanicus*
	Species *transvaalensis*	Subspecies *heidelbergensis*
	Genus *Telanthropus*	Species *sapiens*
	Species *capensis*	Subspecies *rhodesiensis*
	Genus *Zinjanthropus*	Subspecies *neanderthalensis*
	Species *boisei*	Subspecies *sapiens*
	Genus *Meganthropus*	
	Species *palaeojavanicus*	

short, with long trunks and short legs. They would appear to be built to conserve as much heat as possible. Broadly built faces, "double" upper eyelids (epicanthic folds) would seem to be adapted to protect the exposed and vulnerable face and eyes from cold. Conversely, the members of populations living in regions of high temperature yield an advantageous ratio of body surface area to mass, thereby facilitating the maintenance of body heat balance. Because larger-bodied individuals have a smaller surface in proportion to mass, and since volume and mass increase as the cube of the linear dimensions, and surface only as the square, a larger body size serves to reduce heat radiation, and a smaller body size to increase it.

Darwin's phrase "the struggle for existence" was used by him, as he himself stated, in a metaphoric sense. Nevertheless that phrase has been widely misinterpreted to mean, and for this Darwin was not without responsibility in spite of his later attempts at moderation, that there is a "warfare of nature," in which, as Tennyson sang, "Nature red in tooth and claw, shrieks against the creed of man"; in which "the fittest survived and the weakest went to the wall"; in which nature was envisaged as in a constant state of internecine warfare; in which the race went to the swift and the spoils to the strongest.

This rather muscular view of the evolutionary process altogether overemphasized the factor of competition and distorted the meaning of what that term in fact defines. Co-operative behavior, for example, is a form of competition. Insofar as co-operative behavior contributes to the survival of any group, it may be said to be adaptively more fit than behavior not leading to such a result. In the competition for survival co-operative behavior may, therefore, be said to be competitively more successful. Natural selection favors the co-operative as opposed to the unco-operative in the struggle for existence. And in most cases in the state of nature there is no real struggle between populations or individuals, in the sense of active combat, but only in the metaphoric sense of managing to survive and reproduce in an effectively more successful manner, than some other population which is "competing" in the same environment. The populations involved may not even know of each other's existence while engaged in making a living.

The unfortunate habit of thinking in terms of the struggle for existence, by means of which, it is believed, the fittest, that is, "the fightingest" as it was widely interpreted to mean, are alone selected for survival while the weakest are ruthlessly condemned to extinction, is not only an incorrect view of what actually occurs, but is a habit of thought which has done a considerable amount of harm. Only by failing to consider so important an evolutionary factor as co-operation, and by viewing evolution as a process of continuous conflict between all living things, can man be led to conclude that survival or development depends upon successful aggression.

Co-operation is the process of acting together with others to achieve a common purpose and the probability of survival of individuals or groups increases with the degree with which they harmoniously adjust themselves to each other and to their environment. Insofar as co-operative behavior makes for the survival of others it is of high adaptive value and may be expected to spread as a result of natural selection.

Mutations are the raw materials upon which natural selection works. Without mutations there could be no evolution. Mutations come about as a consequence of the basic property of the genetic materials, by means of which these materials replicate themselves.

A mutation is a failure of precision in the basic property of self-copying in a gene, resulting in a transmissible hereditary modification in the expression of a trait. Such errors result in conferring different degrees of biological advantage or disadvantage on those who inherit them. The net effect is differential fertility down the generations, that is, natural selection. The result will be that favorable new mutations or favorable combinations of old mutations will tend to become established as normal in the stock in the place of less favorable ones.

The physical differences existing between the living varieties of man probably represent the end effects of small gene mutations fitting harmoniously into gene systems which remain relatively unaltered.

Under conditions of more or less prolonged *isolation,* the small breeding populations of prehistoric man would tend to become increasingly more distinct from other populations owing to the unique fixation of mutations occurring within the group. In such isolated populations the factor of *genetic drift* (Sewall Wright effect), that is, the accidental increase or decline of mutant genes, resulting in spontaneous random variations in gene frequencies, would be likely to occur. As a result of genetic drift small popula-

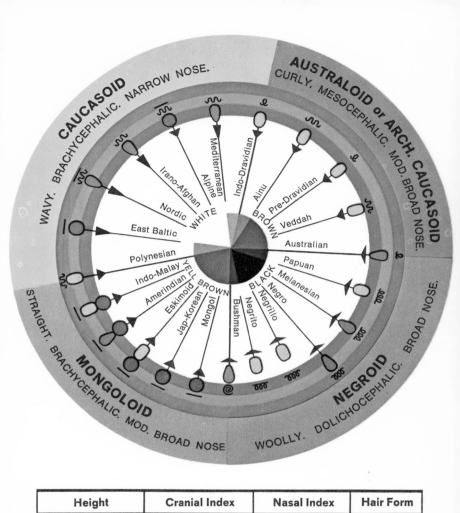

Height	Cranial Index	Nasal Index	Hair Form
1·50 m.–1·60 m.	⬤ Dolichocephalic	▲ Narrow	— Straight
			ᔓ Wavy
1·60 m.–1·70 m.	⬤ Mesocephalic	▲ Moderate	ℓ Curly
			ℓℓℓ Woolly
Over 1·70 m.	⬤ Brachycephalic	◤ Flat or Broad	◎ Spiral

Diagram showing the major and ethnic groups of man usually recognized, together with certain of their physical characters.

tions commencing with similar genetic structure when more or less isolated from one another will in the course of time come to exhibit certain differences. In this way, genes for traits which are neutral, that is, which possess neither a positive nor a negative adaptive value, may spread throughout the population.

Hybridization is the crossing of individuals differing from one another in one or more genes or traits. The two kinds of hybridization are: (1) between individuals, and (2) between populations.

Hybridization between populations leads toward the disappearance of physical and cultural distinctness, except insofar as it produces intermediate ethnic groups on geographic boundaries or within a larger population. In isolation such intermediate groups will develop as distinct populations. Isolation and hybridization followed by isolation have been two of the most important processes in the evolution and diversification of mankind. When individuals or populations of varying heredities hybridize they bring to each other their biologically advantageous traits and thus not only serve to improve the offspring but also to reduce the probability of any harmful traits expressing themselves.

The genetic differences between the ethnic groups of man are not great enough to yield such striking results as hybridization produces between different strains of corn or other plants, or among domestic animals; the phenomenon of hybrid vigor is, however, observable in human crossings. Hybrid vigor or heterosis is the condition, as a result of hybridization, in which the offspring exceed both parental lines in size, fertility, resistance, increased vigor, or other adaptive qualities. Wherever the matter has been investigated, human hybrids show greater fertility than the parental lines and greater resistance to disease. For example, in Tierra del Fuego the unmixed natives succumbed when measles appeared among them, but the hybrids survived. The evidence indicates that in man hybrid vigor expresses itself not so much in changes in physical traits, obvious as these are, as in changes in fertility connected with subtle mechanisms of adaptive value, such, for example, as potential resistance to disease. Differences in fertility within the same population may also be due to slight heterotic effects of many individual genes which in combination serve to produce such differences in fertility. It is also probable that levels of intelligence are not only prevented from declining as a result of hybridization but are also refreshed and enhanced by the introduction of new genes.

Sexual selection as a possible mode of evolution was suggested by Darwin. It was Darwin's thought that males and females differentially tended to select for mating only those having certain characteristics. Even among other animals sexual selection has been shown to play very little if any role as a factor of evolution, and in man, if anyone, it would be the male who would select the female. In most human societies marriage has been strictly regulated and neither males nor females have been free to choose their mates (see pages 115-118). Hence, it is probable that sexual selection has played a very small, if any, role in the evolution of man. In historic times sexual selection has become a factor in the choice of mates. It is, however, difficult to foresee how this may affect the future evolution of man, since, among other things, the variety of grounds upon which unions are contracted change quite rapidly with the vagaries of time.

Social selection refers to the regulation of mating and breeding by means of socially instituted devices which permit unions between approved individuals or groups within a population, and discourage those between the nonapproved individuals and groups. Thus kings and chieftains, for example, are not usually permitted to marry commoners. The members of social classes tend to marry within their own class, but such barriers are everywhere breaking down. While they may have played a significant role in the genetic history of some populations in the past, that role is destined to become increasingly attenuated in modern societies.

THE VARIETIES OF HOMO SAPIENS

All living men (and many earlier forms of men) belong to the species *Homo sapiens*. The species *Homo sapiens* is *polytypic*, that is, it is made up of many types. A polytypic species consists of a group of actually or potentially interbreeding natural populations which is reproductively isolated from other such groups. An appreciable amount of geographic variation occurs between such separated populations. Such populations are the polytypes (subspecies or geographic races). A population is a contiguously distributed grouping of a single species characterized by genetic and cultural continuity through several generations. Groups of populations which do not occur together, which exclude each other geographically, are termed *allopatric*. Populations which occur together,

Negro

English

American Indian
Apache

Japanese

Different ethnic forms of man.

whose areas of distribution coincide or overlap, are termed *sympatric*. Man is a member of a sympatric polytypic species.

The separation, more or less between polytypes, has been geographic or social. Such polytypes are often referred to as *races*, but this word has many considerable objections to it. In biological terms such populations are preferably referred to as *clines*. A *cline* is a character gradient which runs through a continuous population. The term (Latin: *clino*, to lean) refers to the fact that as one passes from place to place in a given direction, the physical characters of the inhabitants of the territories change more or less gradually. Neighboring populations tend to resemble one another more closely than do geographically more remote ones. This is the phenomenon of character gradients. Such populations are clines, and these are the real populations encountered in man, and not *races*, a purely arbitrary concept which is both stultifying and confusing. Furthermore, the term is objectionable on other grounds, and since it has become so hopelessly embarrassed by the false and prejudiced meanings it has universally been made to carry, it is no longer usable. The noncommittal term *ethnic group* will be used, and this may be defined as referring to an arbitrarily recognized group which is characterized by a more or less distinctive assemblage of physical traits, through a common heredity, which distinguishes that group from others within the species. Note that nothing is said of mental, behavioral, or cultural traits, for the simple reason that we have no evidence whatever that such traits are linked with physical traits. This is not to say that some behavioral traits may not be so linked; there are some that probably are, but what these may be, if any, remains for future research to determine. Until that research has been conducted and its findings scientifically confirmed, spec-

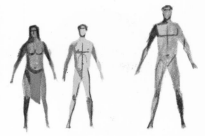

GREATER CONSTITUTIONAL STRENGTH

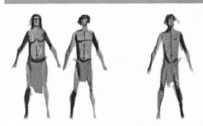

LESS RESISTANCE TO DISEASE

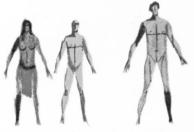

GREATER RESISTANCE TO DISEASE

Hybrid vigor illustrated: the offspring of mating between members of different ethnic groups tend to exhibit greater constitutional strength, greater resistance to disease, and greater intelligence.

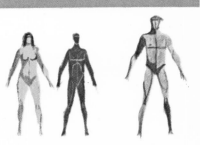

GREATER INTELLIGENCE

ulation on so complex a subject or inadequately controlled studies should not be permitted to pass for anything other than they are.

On the basis of certain superficial characters such as skin color, it is observed that ethnic groups tend to form certain clusters. Black and brown skins yield a cluster of Negroid groups, white skin yields a cluster of White or Caucasoid groups including the Australoid or Archaic White major subgroup, and the populations characterized by a very slight yellowish tinge to the skin yields the cluster of Mongoloids. Such clusters of ethnic groups are known as *major groups*. A major group is comprised of a number of ethnic groups classified together on the basis of their possession of certain common characters which serve to distinguish that major group from others.

Our knowledge of the ethnic groups of man is pitifully small, and the best of ethnic classifications must remain largely arbitrary. Classifications have been urged on the basis of the distribution of blood group genes, but these seem to me even less satisfactory than those made on the basis of the traditional classification, namely, a combination of skin color, hair form, nose shape, and similar traits. Such a classification is admittedly superficial, and may some day be replaced by a genetically sounder one, but until that time is reached, it is best to use a classification that is practical and enables one to distinguish one group from another without the necessity of resorting to elaborate laboratory tests.

THE NEGROID MAJOR GROUP

Skin typically dark brown, often black, and sometimes yellowish-brown. Body hair sparse, head hair varies from tightly curled to peppercorn in form (sparsely distributed tufts). Head long, nose broad and flat with wide nostrils, ears small, lips thick and everted, and some projection of the jaws (prognathism).

Major Group: Negroid

African Negroes
Ethnic Group: a. The True Negro: West Africa, Cameroons, and Congo
                  b. The Half-Hamites: East Africa and East Central Africa

c. Forest Negro: Equatorial and Tropical Africa
d. "Bantu-Speaking Negroids": Central and Southern Africa
e. Nilotic Negro: Eastern Sudan and Upper Nile Valley
f. Bushman: Southern Angola and Northwest Africa
g. Hottentot: South Africa

Oceanic Negroids
Ethnic Group: a. Papuans: New Guinea
                b. Melanesians: Melanesia

African Pygmies or Negrillos
Ethnic Group: a. African Pygmies or Negrillos: Equatorial Africa

Asiatic Pygmies or Negritos
Ethnic Group: a. Andamanese: Andaman Islands
                b. Semang: Central Malay Peninsula and East Sumatra
                c. Philippine Negritos: Philippine Islands

Oceanic Pygmies or Negritos
Ethnic Group: a. New Guinea Pygmies: New Guinea

THE CAUCASOID MAJOR GROUP

This major group is often called "White." The term is an inaccurate one because the group includes many people of dark skin color. The name "Caucasoid" was given to the group by the father of physical anthropology, Johann Friedrich Blumenbach (1752-1840), who named the type after a female skull from Georgia in the Caucasus.

Skin color varies from "white" to dark brown. Hair over the whole body is usually well developed, varying from silky straight to varying degrees of curliness. It is almost never woolly, rarely frizzly, and seldom coarse as in Mongoloids. All forms of head shape occur, with the general tendency toward broad-headedness. The nose is comparatively narrow and projecting, the cheek bones are generally

75

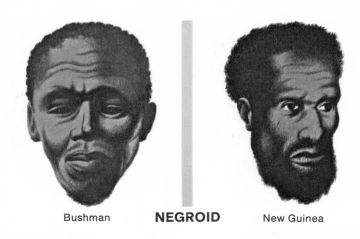

Bushman   **NEGROID**   New Guinea

not prominent, and the lips tend to be thin. The face tends to be straight (orthognathic), owing to the nonprojecting jaws, the chin is well developed, and the palate and teeth smaller than in other peoples.

Major Group: Caucasoid

Ethnic Group:
- a. Basic Mediterranean: Borderlands of the Mediterranean Basin
- b. Atlanto-Mediterranean: Middle East, eastern Balkans, East Africa, Portugal, Spain, British Isles
- c. Irano-Afghan Mediterranean: Iran, Afghanistan, parts of India, Arabia, and North Africa
- d. Nordic: Central Europe, Scandinavia, and neighboring regions
- e. East Baltic: East Baltic regions
- f. Lapps: Northern Scandinavia, Kola Peninsula
- g. Alpine: France along the Alps to Russia
- h. Dinaric: Eastern Alps from Switzerland to Albania, Asia Minor, and Syria
- k. Indo-Dravidians: India and Ceylon
- i. Armenoids: Asia Minor
- j. Hamites: North and East Africa
- l. Polynesians: Polynesia (Central Pacific)

76

Polynesian   **CAUCASOID**   Italian

Eskimo   **MONGOLOID**   Malay

Ainu   **AUSTROLOID**   Australian Aborigines

Right eye showing medial epicanthic fold.

Major Sub-Group: Australoid or Archaic Caucasoid

Ethnic Group: a. Australian aborigines: Australia
                  b. Veddah: Ceylon
                  c. Pre-Dravidian: India
                  d. Ainu: Japan, Hokkaido (Yezo), and Sakhalin Islands

THE MONGOLOID MAJOR GROUP

The skin has a very slight yellowish tinge. Head hair is generally black and straight; body hair is sparse. The face tends to be flat, the cheek bones strongly developed and projecting laterally, and a median fold of skin, the epicanthic fold, overhangs the inner angle of the eye opening. The nose is flat or low at the root, the bridge is low, and the wings of the nostrils of medium spread. The lips are of medium fullness and the chin well developed. The incisor teeth tend to be scooped out behind like a shovel, hence, "shovel-shaped"; the upper jaw has a marked tendency to project slightly upward and forward, giving the appearance in many individuals, particularly males, of "buck teeth." The head tends to be broad (brachycephalic), and the cranial capacity is among the largest in the human species, frequently reaching 1,700 cc.

Major Group: Mongoloid

Classical Mongoloids
Ethnic Group: a. An undetermined number of ethnic groups in

the older populations of Tibet, Mongolia, China, Korea, Japan, and Siberia, including such tribes as the Buriats east and west of Lake Baikal, the Koryak of northern Siberia, the Gilyak of northernmost Sakhalin and the mainland north of the Amur estuary (who appear to have mixed with the Ainu), and the Goldi on the Lower Amur and Ussuri.

Arctic Mongoloids
Ethnic Group: a. Eskimo: Extreme northeast of Asia, Arctic coast of North America, Greenland. The type includes the Aleuts of the Aleutian Islands, and the Reindeer and coastal Chukchee of Northeastern Siberia.
b. Evenki or true Tungus (Americanoids): Mongolia, Siberia, Asiatic highlands north of Himalayas.
c. Kamchatdales: Kamchatka
d. Samoyedes: Kola Peninsula, White Sea and Yenisei regions.

The Mongoloids of the extreme northeast of the Asiatic continent are distinguished as the Paleoasiatics. These are considered to be the complex of ancient populations of Asia who early migrated to this extreme peripheral region. The populations believed to have migrated later into the northeast of the Asiatic continent are known as the Neoasiatics.

Paleoasiatics: Chukchee, Koryak, Kamchatdale, Gilyak, Eskimo, Aleut, Yukaghir, Chuvantzi, Ostyak of Yenisei, Ainu.

Neoasiatics: Finnic tribes, Samoyedic tribes, Turkic, including Yakut, Mongolic, Tungusic.

American Indians
Ethnic Group: a. An undetermined number of ethnic groups of North, Middle, Central, and South America.

Indo-Malay
Ethnic Group: a. Indonesian: Southern China, Indo-China, Burma, Thailand, Interior of Malay Archipelago.

b. Malay: In addition to Indonesian distribution, Malay Peninsula, Dutch East Indies, Philippines, Okinawa, and adjacent islands.

CONCLUSIONS

It should be clearly understood that the classification of the ethnic groups of man given above is an arbitrary one. Many others could be, and have been, given. Such classifications are to be regarded as no more than convenient devices for the purposes of communication. The physical differences upon which such classifications are based express differences in the biological history of the labeled populations. When these differences are considered and evaluated they are seen to be relatively few in number compared to the overwhelming number of likenesses, and they are seen to be of a nature which does not render any one of the groups concerned either biologically superior or inferior to the other.

"RACE" AND RACISM

The belief that some men are born to be slaves and some to be masters is much older than Aristotle who first put it in those words in *The Politics*. But from *The Politics* to this day the idea that some groups of men are born less well endowed with intelligence than others has steadily grown until it has assumed the form of *racism*. Racism is the doctrine that stresses the importance of what is called "race" as a basis for discrimination and intergroup action, especially for segregation and superior rights for one group over others. What is called "race" by racists, and by others who are not racists but simply affected by the unsound ideas which are too often taken for granted, is that there exist certain inherent differences between "races" which are recognizable as differences in intelligence, traits of character, general behavior, creative ability, and emotions. Such differences are found to exist among virtually all populations, and the racists and others conclude from their existence that they are due to innately determined biological differences. But the evidence of history and of experience tells us that such behavioral differences are more likely to be due to cultural factors, that people of a common historical and cultural back-

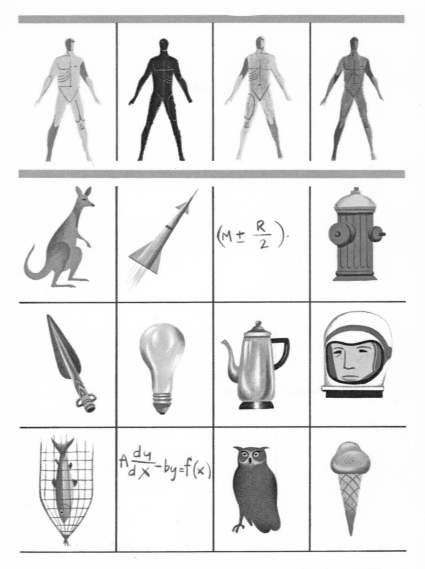

Absurdities of culturally conditioned intelligence tests. Members of different cultures unfamiliar with the cultural products of other cultures are unlikely to do well on tests which incorporate such items.

ground are likely to differ from one another for those reasons and not for any others. This is not to assert that there may not be some group factors of a biological nature which have some influence in affecting the behavioral differences between populations. Such factors may exist, but if they do, they cannot be of very great significance, and in spite of many attempts to discover them, no one has thus far succeeded in doing so.

To attribute the differences obtained in intelligence tests on different populations to differences in innate intelligence is to commit the error of failing to realize that what intelligence tests measure is practical performance in problem solving. Even when applied to members of the same socioeconomic class and culture, these tests constitute no more than the very crudest measure of innate ability, because they make no allowance whatever for the differences in experience which the tested individuals have undergone. Individuals with the same genetic potentials for intelligence with different backgrounds of experience will fare very differently on IQ tests. The same individual with increase in experience and maturity will generally show an increase in IQ score. Cross-cultural intelligence tests, that is, tests of intelligence which allow for differences in the ways of life in which individuals are conditioned in different cultures, have never been devised, and it is utterly absurd

BACKGROUND FACTORS ENTER INTO TEST PERFORMANCE

An intelligence tester among the Kentucky "poor whites" presented the following problem to a boy being tested: "If you went to the store and bought six cents' worth of candy and gave the clerk 10 cents, what change would you receive?" The boy replied, "I never had 10 cents, and if I had I wouldn't spend it for candy, and anyway candy is what your mother makes." The intelligence-tester tried again, reformulating the problem as follows: "If you had taken 10 cows to pasture for your father and 6 of them strayed away, how many would you have left to drive home?" The boy replied, "We don't have 10 cows, but if we did and I lost 6, I wouldn't dare go home." The intelligence-tester made one last effort: "If there were 10 children in a school and 6 of them were out with measles, how many would there be in school?" The question was no sooner asked than it was answered: "None, because the rest would be afraid of catching it too."

Reported in S. L. Pressey, *Psychology and the Newer Education*, 1933, p. 237.

to draw inferences about the intelligence of different ethnic groups on the basis of tests which were never devised for this purpose and to which they cannot legitimately be applied. Nevertheless such tests have been indiscriminately applied and the most far-reaching conclusions drawn from them. The inferences unfavorable to the intelligence of the people on whom such indignities have been visited reflect rather more upon the intelligence of those who have failed to see the errors they were committing than upon the people tested. The evidence, such as it is, indicates that within every ethnic group there is to be found approximately the same range of temperament and intelligence.

When opportunities for the development of innate abilities tend to be equalized, and this includes early upbringing and a continuing comparable environment, the intelligence scores of the members of different ethnic groups also tend to become equalized.

When we inquire why it is that the cultures and cultural achievements of different ethnic groups differ from one another as much as they often do, the answer appears to be that they do so for much the same reasons as individuals differ from one another in their ordinary abilities, because of the differences in the history of experience which each of them has undergone. Always allowing for the possibility that some genetic factors may be involved, in the final analysis the answer is no more complex than that.

In the balance of humanity no group of human beings is of lesser value than any other. Under the enabling conditions which should constitute the birthright of every individual of every population, all groups of human beings possess the potentialities for contributing in a substantial manner to the welfare and the achievement of humanity.

It should be clearly understood that equality of opportunity is a principle which does not imply biological equality. The idea that all men are born equal refers to their birthright: equality of opportunity for the development of their innate potentialities, and in no way is based or depends on the idea that human beings or groups are equal in endowment. The idea of equality is simple: it holds that by virtue of the fact that a person is a human being he has the right, and it should be the obligation of every society to see to it that he enjoys the right, to realize to the optimum whatever potentialities he is endowed with and to fulfill himself in relation to his fellow men.

Man: The Cultural Creature

As a consequence of the loss of his instincts, man has been forced to create responses to his environment which enable him to live in it and survive at least as successfully as other animals who are largely dependent upon their instincts. Instead of being dependent upon instincts, man is dependent upon learned responses to meet the challenges of his environment. Everything a man does and knows as a human being, apart from his organic functions, he has learned from other human beings. As a result of this capacity and necessity for learning man has built up a great body of knowledge and skills and artifacts which enable him not only to live and survive in, but also to establish some degree of mastery over, the great variety of environments in which he finds himself. This non-organic, learned, man-made part of the environment is man's *culture*. It is the socially transmitted body of customs, knowledge, and skills which enable the individual to function as a member of his society. A culture-less human being—and there have been many

Uprights and lintel, Stonehenge. About 1,500 B.C.

such—is unable to function as a member of society. Culture is man's principal means of adapting himself to his environment. Man, indeed, is the only creature who has moved virtually entirely into the new zone of adaptation of culture, from the world of functioning largely at the organic animal level, or *zoösphere*, to the psychosocial world of largely mental functioning, or *psychosphere*.

Instead of having to submit to the environments in which he finds himself, as is the case with other animals, man through culture and the use of his great intelligence has the ability to create his own environment. He provides himself with artificial lungs in order to spend hours swimming like a fish; he builds airplanes in which he flies faster than any bird; he tunnels the earth, bridges rivers, and in a few seconds is able to communicate with other men thousands of miles away. In cold climates instead of growing a coat of hair, he makes one and clothes himself in it. In hot climates he protects himself from the rays of the sun by smearing himself with earth, or by taking shelter within the houses he builds. In the societies of the western world man now makes his own climate within his homes and public buildings with air-conditioning and heating. Through cultural means he has more than doubled his life expectancy in those parts of the world in which he has brought his knowledge and intelligence to bear upon the problems of public health, and by the same means he has increased his numbers at such a rate that he is now not only the most widely distributed animal on this planet, but at his present rate of increase threatens to become one of the most densely distributed of all animals.

Culture is the means not only for controlling but for changing the pressures of natural selection, and thus culture constitutes an important influence in the physical as well as the cultural evolution of man. The development of tools has almost certainly been influential in reducing the size of man's teeth and jaws. Marriage regulations that made it obligatory to marry outside one's own group or tribe would have genetic effects, over the course of time, different from those which would result from marriage regulations which required all marriages to take place between cross-cousins. The selection of preferred types of personality would make for the establishment of genotypes with the preferred traits. Sexual selection is coming to play an increasingly more important role in contemporary societies in perpetuating preferred physical types.

As man advances in civilization his scientific discoveries and technical progress enable him to provide enormous numbers of individuals with remedies and supports for defects, which under less culturally advanced conditions and in the absence of such practical remedies would have resulted in their early demise or irreversible maldevelopment.

The technically highly advanced cultures of the world today provide a place for virtually every kind of physical and mental type. In technically less advanced cultures the maldeveloped infant is not encouraged to survive, and the individual of biologically low adaptive fitness in one or more traits is not, as in the more civilized cultures, supported and compensated for by medical or social agencies. In order to survive, nonliterate societies in general require the active labor of everyone capable of working; it is severely handicapping for them to have to carry the burden of an incapacitated member. But as nonliterate societies develop in their ability to

The Plumed Serpent of Quetzalcooate. Mexican, Fifth Century.

control the environment, they increasingly tend to make provision for the infirm and the old.

Culture does not, as is sometimes claimed, suspend the operation of natural selection, but simply causes it to be redirected. Natural selection continues to act upon man, but now it is in relation to the new environments which he has created and in which he has his being. Fitness is always a matter of fitness in relation to some part or parts of the environment. No one is ever equally fit in relation to all parts of the environment. Within his cultural environment man is still subject to the action of natural selection, but in ways modified by that cultural environment. Biological damage which, in the absence of cultural arrangements such as medicine and other social services, would express itself, in the presence of such cultural agencies is either reduced or avoided.

Culture can, therefore, help to avoid or reduce the biological and social damage that would otherwise be done to many individuals and their society. Thus, while culture can to some extent change the course of natural selection, it cannot altogether abrogate it. But through cultural means man can increasingly consciously take a dominant hand in the direction of his own future evolution. Culture has given man the greatest power over his environment, and it could give him an equally great power over himself. The difficulty seems to lie not so much in the failure to exercise that power, as in the confusion which exists in what is exercised.

By virtue of the fact that man is so educable a creature, he is capable of learning and acquiring more information than any other creature on this earth. However, he is capable of learning

Roman head of young man wearing athlete's hat. Republican Period.

more unsound things as well as sound ones than any other creature, and such learning does not make so much for intelligence as for confusion. The unreal can be every bit as real as the real if one only thinks it so, and nonsense will pass as common sense if only a sufficient number of individuals call it so. Every culture is characterized by an amalgam of sound and unsound ideas concerning the nature of man and the meaning and purpose of existence, and it is this confused amalgam of ideas which, in every society, has thus far constituted the chief impediment to man's more successful mastery of himself. In time, perhaps through the successful integration of reason, science, the humanities, and religion, something of that mastery may be achieved. It would appear, at any rate, that it is in that direction that mankind is evolving.

Culture as the way of life of a people is principally, if not entirely, the expression of the past history of the particular culture. Until evidence to the contrary is forthcoming, it may be safely assumed that cultures differ from one another principally because of the differences in the history of experience which each of those cultures express in the forms they exhibit. Populations which from prehistoric times have been long isolated from other populations are in many ways likely to be culturally less developed than populations which have enjoyed a good deal of cultural interchange with other populations. For example, when one considers the populations living in the southern extremities of the various continents and those populations living in the central regions of such continents or in the desert or semidesert regions, such, for instance, as the Tierra del Fuegoans of the southernmost tip of South America, the Hottentots and Bushmen of Southern Africa and the Kalahari Desert, the Andaman Islanders of the southernmost tip of India, the Australian aborigines, and the Congo pygmies, and before they were destroyed by the white man, the Tasmanians, all are characterized by the fact that they never developed agriculture and therefore lived by food-gathering and hunting. A trait shared in common by the Andaman Islanders and the Congo pygmies is that neither of these peoples knew how to make fire.

The southernmost tips of continents, the southernmost islands of large land masses, and the interiors of continents are likely to be largely bypassed by migrating populations, so that the populations occupying such areas remain isolated from the main streams of

In using Table VIII it should be understood that the approximate dates assigned to the different "Ages" refer only in a general way to the areas mentioned. As the table indicates these "Ages" were not everywhere contemporaneous. The different "Ages" do not afford a measure of time, for they varied in different parts of the world both in the time of their appearance and in their duration, while some of the cultural stages they embrace never appeared at all, but were completely skipped in the progress from one cultural stage to another. These ages are therefore to be regarded as *cultural or technological* rather than as chronological periods. It is extremely important to grasp this fact. There was no world-wide evolution from one stage to another, each stage represents an industrial revolution in the manufacture of tools which occurred in different places at different times, nor did the several stages begin and end simultaneously all over the world. Thus, to give a simple example, the Early Iron Age began in Asia Minor about 1200 B.C., in central Europe about 900 B.C., in China about 700 B.C., in southern England about 600 B.C., in Japan about A.D. 900, and in Fiji about 1870. In the last column names in *italics* refer to types which are uncertainly dated.

CHRONOLOGICAL-CULTURAL TABLE OF THE DIVISIONS OF PREHISTORY AND C

	Stage	Alpine and Scandinavian glacial oscillations with corresponding changes of sea level and climate		Northwestern Continental Europe
	POWER TOOLS		A.D. 1900	Rise of Age of power tool
	OLD NEW STEEL	Present conditions of Mya Period in Baltic area	A.D. 1850	Steel Age develops
			A.D. 1700	Steel (carbonised iron)
			A.D. 1000	
Late			A.D. 500	Viking Age
Middle	IRON		50 B.C.	Roman Period of Iron Age
Early			500 B.C.	Iron Age introduced
	BRONZE		1,000 B.C.	Northern Bronze Age
			1,500 B.C.	
			2,000 B.C.	
Late		Final land rise in Baltic area or Late Tapes Period		Northern Neolithic
Middle	NEOLITHIC		2,500 B.C.	
Early			3,000 B.C.	Ertebølle Mesolithic
			3,500 B.C.	
			4,000 B.C.	
	MESOLITHIC	Sea rising, Ragunda retreat, with Littorina Sea (Early Tapes Period) preceded by late Ancyclus Lake	5,000 B.C.	
			6,000 B.C.	Maglemose Mesolithic
			7,000 B.C.	
		Ragunda pause with Ancyclus Lake		Tanged Point Cultures (Lyngby etc.)
			10,000 B.C.	
Upper		Fini-glacial pause with Baltic ice-lake	13,500 B.C.	
		Gothi-glacial retreat with Baltic ice-lake	15,000 B.C.	
		Gothi-glacial pause with Baltic ice-lake	20,000 B.C.	
		Würm or Achen and Dani-glacial retreats with Frankfort and Pomeranian pause. Flandrian terrace	25,000 B.C.	
			40,000 B.C.	
Middle	PALEOLITHIC	Würm and Brandenburg or Dani-glacial advances, 4th Glacial	50,000 B.C.	
			75,000 B.C.	
		Riss retreat with Monastrian terrace, 3rd Interglacial. Hot summer		
			150,000 B.C.	
		Riss and Polonian advances, 3rd Glacial	250,000 B.C.	
		Mindel retreat with Tyrrhenian terrace, 2nd Interglacial		
Lower		Mindel advance, 2nd Glacial	400,000 B.C.	
			500,000 B.C.	
		Günz retreat with Milazzian terrace, 1st Interglacial		
		Günz advance, 1st Glacial. Pleistocene	600,000 B.C.	
		Pliocene. Donau with Sicilian terrace	1,000,000 B.C.	

Principal Culture Stages of Europe, Egypt and the Near East

West Central Europe	Near East	Egypt	Human Types
Tene Iron Age			
lstatt Iron Age			
e Bronze Age (Urnfield)			
ddle Bronze Age (Tumulus)			
·ly Bronze Age (Aunjetitz)			
e Neolithic (Danubian III, stern and corded-battle axe mixture)			Persisting varieties of *Homo sapiens*
nubian Neolithic II and West- Neolithic Cultures			
movement of Danubian Neolic peoples into Central Europe	Early Dynastic, Proliterate	Dynastic Egypt	
	Warka, Ubaid, Halaf	Nakada II (Gerzean)	
denoisian, Azilian,	Hassuna, Matarrah	Nakada I (Amratian)	
turian and other	Basal Mersin	Badarian	
solithic cultures	Early Neolithic, Jericho and Jarmo	Tasian	
	Natufian		Chancelade
agdalenian	Atlitian		Předmost, *Baker's Hole*, Rhodesian, Crô-magnon, Châtelpèrron, Grimaldi, Africanthropus, Solo
lutrean	Aurignacian		
rignacian and Perigordian		Sebilian of Nile silts	
ousterian	Levalloiso-Mousterian		Boskop
heulian, Levalloisian, yacian and Micoquian	Acheulian	"Egyptian Levalloisian" industry of 10 m. Nile terrace	Florisbad, Skhūl, Gibraltar II, *Wadjak*, *Rhodesian*
			Tabūn, Neanderthal, Ehringsdorf, Fontéchevade, Montmaurin
erived implements			*Rabut, Sidi Abderrahman*
bevillian, Acheulian, Clactonian d Levalloisian	Acheulian	Acheulian industry of 50 m. Nile terrace	*Steinheim*, Swanscombe, Heidelberg, Atlanthropus, Sinanthropus, Pithecanthropus erectus
erived implements			Pithecanthropus robustus
oto-Abbevillian industry from low Cromer forest beds	Abbevillian	Abbevillian and Early Abbevillian of 100 m. Nile terrace	Pithecanthropus (Modjokerto), *Meganthropus*
			Zinjanthopus, Homo habilis

cross-cultural fertilization and therefore remain in many ways rather more primitive than those populations that have enjoyed the advantages of such cross-cultural fertilization.

When we say that such cultures remain in many ways more "primitive" than those which have enjoyed the advantages of association and the stimulating exchange of ideas and skills with other peoples, we mean that in certain respects that they are closer in some of their ways of life to those of earlier than to those of later times. But such peoples should not be referred to as "primitive" because in many other respects they are usually far more advanced than were their prehistoric ancestors, and within the limits placed upon them by their environment they are often very highly developed, in some respects even more developed than the average member of highly civilized western societies. For example, they generally have a much fuller command of the linguistic subtleties of language and the various elements of their culture, they have a much more intimate understanding of and communion with the world of nature, and they possess a thoroughly more profound comprehension of the relation of man to his fellows. Furthermore, every human population has an equally long history. "Nonliterate" peoples, as the anthropologist prefers to call them, because they do not have writing or a written history, differ culturally from other nonliterate and literate peoples principally because each of them has had a different kind of learning experience. All the evidence that we have points strongly to the fact that as opportunities tend to be equalized, every population of human beings is capable of learning what every other population has ever learned. It may be that in some populations there are different frequencies of genes for different kinds of achievement. We do not know. Such differences, if they exist, would be statistical and would have no significance whatsoever, for the fact is that individual variability would be such in every population that individuals running the gamut from mediocrity to genius would be found in every population. The probabilities are high that in the course of human evolution the highest premium was put not upon those individuals possessing certain specific abilities, but rather upon the general trait of plasticity, or educability and co-operativeness. If this was so, and such evidence

"Fish at Play." Australian aboriginal painting on Eucalyptus bark, Arnhem Land. (Courtesy, Quantas Airlines)

93

as we have would indicate that it was, then it is highly improbable that any significant differences exist among the various ethnic groups and populations of mankind for the development of culture and for cultural achievement. Wherever this assumption has been put to the test it has been fully justified, and the whole of cultural history testifies to its soundness.

Few, if any, nonliterate peoples have ever been given full equality by their "superiors." But even under conditions of considerable cultural inequality there have been some remarkable demonstrations of the ability of nonliterate and other disadvantaged peoples. One of the most interesting of these concerns a school populated entirely by Australian aboriginal children. Writing in 1899, the Rev. John Mathew states, "In schools it has often been observed that aboriginal children learn quite as easily and rapidly as children of European parents. In fact, the aboriginal school at Ramahyuck, in Victoria, stood for three consecutive years the highest of all state schools of the colony in examination results, *obtaining one hundred per cent of marks*." (Mathew's italics.) In recent years it has been discovered that Australian aborigines are astonishingly gifted artists, though no one would have suspected this from their traditional forms of art. Indeed, their traditionally stylized art was often cited as evidence of their "low mental development." It has long been known that American Indians do not do well on the white man's intelligence tests. The over-all average Indian IQ is 80. But when American Indian children are raised in white foster homes their IQ rises to an average of 102, a gain of 22 points. The average IQ of brothers and sisters of these children who were still living on the Indian reservation was only 87.5.

As a result of a fortunate find of oil on their lands, the Osage Indians of Oklahoma have been able to afford their children above-average opportunities, with the result that the Osage children now obtain a score of 104 on the Goodenough "Draw-a-Man" test, while the white children in the neighborhood score an average of one point less. On a second test which made use of language, the average IQ of the Osage children was 100, while the white average was 98. This statistical difference is not significant. What *is* significant is that as a result of improved socioeconomic conditions the Osage children were given advantages which made it possible for them to perform on a basis of equality with the white children.

Even more striking is a 1960 report on the educational achievement of Negro pupils, following the desegregation of schools in Washington. At sixth grade level the U.S. norm in performance is 6.6 grades. The median grade levels for the Negro pupils, which previously ranged from 5.4 to 6.1 in different subjects, rose to levels between 6.0 and 6.6. The normal rate of improvement between the third and sixth grades is 3.4 years. For these students it was 3.5 and 3.9 years. The performance of the children in the earlier grades was even better.

THE CRITERIA, CONDITIONS, AND DEVELOPMENT OF CULTURE

Cultural traits are distinguished by the following criteria: they are (1) invented, (2) transmitted, and (3) perpetuated. While some animals have a strictly limited capacity for culture, man's cultural capacities are unlimited. The conditions necessary for the development of human culture are (1) freedom from instincts predetermining responses to the environment, replaced by (2) a highly developed capacity for learning, (3) a prolonged dependency or learning period, (4) a highly developed capacity for problem solving, that is, intelligence, (5) powerful potentialities for the development of symbolic thought, (6) speech, and (7) a highly developed capacity for innovation or the creation of novelty.

A creature with all these capacities born into a human environment will take on the cultural characteristics of that particular environment regardless of his major group or ethnic origins. No other living creature can do so. Not only is the creature endowed with these capacities capable of being culturalized in any culture, but by virtue of the possession of those traits that creature is able to interact with the environment in an actively creative manner. Thus, every normal member of a culture is a potential contributor to the development of that culture.

A social state exists when two or more individuals interact with one another. The nuclear or biological family, consisting of a male and female forming a more or less permanent union and their children, is the basic unit of society. Out of the satisfaction of the needs of one another, of the dependent infants and older children, there will result a division of labor and of roles. Obligations not only to the family but to the society will be entailed. These obligations will be of a legal, economic, educational, and political nature. And the responses thus made, which essentially grow out of the social satisfaction of basic needs and the needs derived from the satisfaction of these, in turn lead to the development of all those cultural responses we know.

Communication

The functional trait most characteristic of man is speech or language. Speech is the communication of ideas by articulate sounds. As such speech is the most important and useful of all man's tools. Concerning the origin of language we know nothing. It would, however, seem probable that the earliest men already had some language. A language is a convention among men that certain combinations of sounds shall be used with common meanings. The meanings are symbols, that is, they represent ideas which stand for things not actually present.

Every language has a grammar, and the languages of nonliterate peoples are not less complex, and in a number of ways are often more efficient and ingenious, than the languages of literate societies.

Writing was invented very late in the history of man, about 3500 B.C. in Sumer in Mesopotamia, the birthplace of civilization itself. Precursors of writing are known from cave and rock drawings, message sticks, tree inscriptions, and bark letters. Many peoples have had a form of pictographic writing, but this was of a very limited character. The Maya Indians of Yucatán independently invented writing, but precisely when they did so is at present unknown.

The Physical Environment: Man and Nature

It is natural for man to be unnatural, to improve upon nature, and in many ways to control nature and cause it to do his bidding. In moving into the cultural dimension, far from leaving the physical environment behind him man has learned to enter more fully into it and exercise an increasing mastery over it. He may wear his culture like a diadem, but its setting is always the physical environment. Within that physical setting man has worked out the most ingenious designs for living, everywhere limited to some extent by the environment, but everywhere also exercising some measure of control over it.

That the physical environment places certain limitations upon man's inventiveness should be clear. For example, in desert or semidesert environments in which there are no large bodies of water it is highly unlikely that anyone will ever invent a boat. We can be equally certain that in such regions, in which water is a problem of survival, there will be certain cultural practices designed to secure water. These will take the form of prayer, incantation, magic, and the exploitation of every possible physical means of securing water. Thus, the Bushmen of the Kalahari Desert are able

Australian aboriginal extracting water from roots of small tree, during drought by burning leafy part.

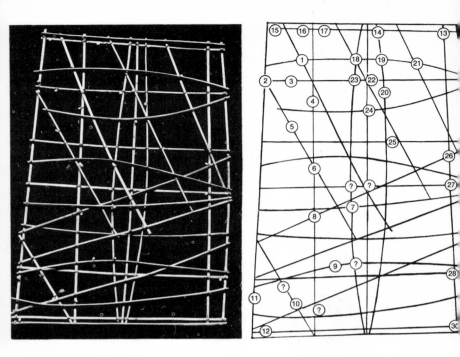

Left: Micronesian navigation chart showing the Marshall Islands. (Courtesy, British Museum) In general the straight horizontal and vertical sticks are primarily intended as supports for the map, though incidentally they may represent the direction of the swells. The diagonal and curved sticks represent the swells produced by the prevailing winds which travel in a direction at right angles to each stick on the concave side. The shells tied to the sticks represent the position of most of the islands in the group. The islands are remarkably accurately located. Right: Key-Plan of the Micronesian navigation chart. (Courtesy of the Royal Anthropological Institute)

to detect from the appearance of the sand where water might be sucked out through a straw. The Central Australian aborigines when they find the land utterly devoid of water dig up bushes and small trees, light a fire under the leafy ends, and collect the sap as it runs from the roots.

The Bushmen and Australian aborigines, like other nonliterate peoples inhabiting arid environments in which the poverty of the soil, the scarcity of water, and the sparsity of plants and animals is such as literally to force them to adopt a wandering, food-gathering, hunting way of life, present clear examples of the limiting

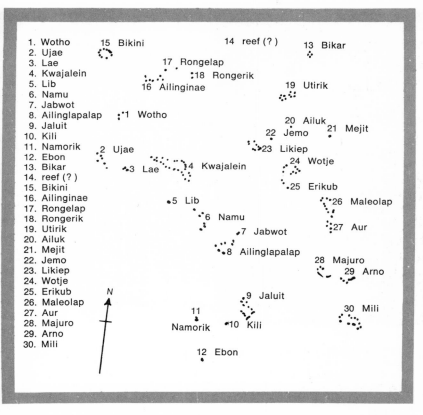

1. Wotho
2. Ujae
3. Lae
4. Kwajalein
5. Lib
6. Namu
7. Jabwot
8. Ailinglapalap
9. Jaluit
10. Kili
11. Namorik
12. Ebon
13. Bikar
14. reef (?)
15. Bikini
16. Ailinginae
17. Rongelap
18. Rongerik
19. Utirik
20. Ailuk
21. Mejit
22. Jemo
23. Likiep
24. Wotje
25. Erikub
26. Maleolap
27. Aur
28. Majuro
29. Arno
30. Mili

15 Bikini
14 reef (?)
13 Bikar
17 Rongelap
:18 Rongerik
16 Ailinginae
19 Utirik
:1 Wotho
20 Ailuk
22 Jemo
21 Mejit
2 Ujae
:23 Likiep
3 Lae
4 Kwajalein
24 Wotje
25 Erikub
5 Lib
26 Maleolap
6 Namu
27 Aur
7 Jabwot
8 Ailinglapalap
28 Majuro
29 Arno
N
9 Jaluit
11 Namorik
10 Kili
30 Mili
12 Ebon

Chart of the Marshall Islands. The left-hand column refers to the position of the islands as marked by the shells on the navigation chart on the opposite page.

effects of the environment upon the way of life of a people. The development of agriculture is not possible in regions such as these, where it sometimes fails to rain for years on end.

Australian aborigines living in the vicinity of large rivers or along the seacoast have devised rafts and boats and a variety of fishing methods.

The Bushmen and Australian aborigines living in regions of high temperature and being nomadic require no permanent houses, and so build only temporary shelters or windbreaks, which serve to protect them from the wind and to give them shade from the burning

sun. Nudity is the rule because clothes are not needed. Where, however, as in the Arctic, the Eskimo finds himself in a freezing environment he clothes himself in the skins of animals. When he needs shelter he builds a house from ice blocks which he cuts—the only material available to him for the purpose. Agriculture is obviously impossible in the Arctic wastes, and the Eskimo is forced by his environment to wander in search of his food, which consists mainly of fish, seal, an occasional bird, caribou where these are available, eked out by occasional mosses and lichens which may be revealed in summer when, in certain spots, the ice melts. Like most other peoples, the Eskimo takes full advantage of every means at his disposal to win in the struggle for survival.

This is, perhaps, the point at which to note and underscore the fact that all peoples who live in the food-gathering-hunting (and fishing) states are characteristically co-operative and peaceful. These peoples have a highly developed feeling of responsibility toward one another, and this is seen especially in their sensitive responses to the needs of children. The unco-operative individual

Independent invention: combining the principles of the cantilever and suspension bridges, this bridge crosses the Gauil River in central New Guinea.

in nonliterate societies is a rarity and tends to be regarded as unbalanced. The precariousness of life in such environments renders it culturally obligatory for everyone to be involved in his fellow's welfare. It is only when, through the development of his cultures, the pressures of the physical environment become relaxed that men can become unco-operative, isolated, and preoccupied with the satisfaction of their own needs with more or less complete indifference to the needs of others.

Thus, from the conditions described we can deduce several principles. The first of these is *the principle of limited possibilities,* which states that the limitations imposed by the physical environment will tend to limit what can be culturally developed under those conditions. Similarly, a special case of the principle applies within cultures to the limitations imposed by conditions of use upon various artifacts. There are not many ways in which one can make an ax or an oar. The conditions under which such artifacts are used will largely determine their form.

A second principle is *the principle of convergence,* which states that under similar economic and social conditions of life cultures will exhibit a number of basic similarities.

These principles, of course, hold true in a general way. While it is true that under similar challenges of the environment different populations will tend to respond in similar ways, and thus independently invent such responses, the principle of convergence cannot be universally applied to mean that under similar conditions similar responses will *always* be made by different populations. Thus, the returning boomerang was invented by the Australian aborigines, and occurs nowhere else outside Australia, even though many hunting peoples in other parts of the world would have found such an implement extremely useful. However, maritime peoples, like the nonliterate Polynesians and the highly civilized Europeans, who habitually made long journeys by sea, would have had a pressing need for navigation charts, and therefore were forced to invent them. The Polynesians developed quite elaborate ones made of sticks and shells tied together, while the Europeans drew theirs on parchment and later on paper.

Deep rivers at the bottom of high cliffs have everywhere to be bridged, and it is not, therefore, altogether surprising that feats of engineering in bridge building have been achieved by nonliterate

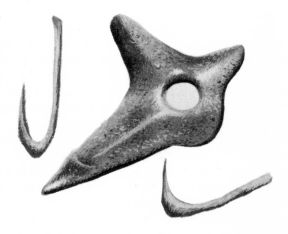

peoples which rival those of the most highly trained bridge builders of literate societies. Thus, when in the nineteen thirties the non-literate peoples of New Guinea living beyond the Bismarck Range were discovered, it was found that they had built bridges across their rivers embodying the principles of the cantilever and suspension bridges. But not all nonliterate peoples have met the challenges presented by such rivers with bridges of this sort. Some, like the Congo pygmy, while occasionally building a simple bridge will, as likely as not, prefer to swing across the river from a liana strung from a tall tree.

On the basis of their economic activities human societies can be classified under the following four different categories:

     I. Food-gatherers, hunters, and fishers
    II. Agricultural peoples
   III. Pastoral peoples
    IV. Artisans

Food-gatherers, Hunters, and Fishers

Examples of this category have already been given in the form of the Bushmen, Australian aborigines, and Eskimos, the latter being mainly hunters and fishers. Some other peoples falling into this category are the Congo pygmies, who are mainly hunters, the Negritos of Malaya, the "Digger" Indians and some others of California, who are mainly food-gatherers. This was the stage of development in which prehistoric man lived for the greater part of his history.

Agricultural Peoples

These are peoples who live mainly by the cultivation of plant foods. Agriculture was probably independently invented by different human populations at different times in various parts of the world. Its earliest practice thus far discovered dates back some 9,000 years to Wadi-en-Natuf in Palestine and Neolithic Jericho. Agriculture probably preceded the domestication of animals, with the exception of the dog, which is usually the only animal that food-gathering-hunting-fishing peoples have. The dog was first domesticated in the Mesolithic (the Middle Stone Age which followed the Old Stone Age or Paleolithic) and was not normally used as a food animal. The discovery of agriculture occurred in the Neolithic or New Stone Age (characterized by ground and pol-

103

ished stone tools, weaving, pottery, nonbronze and ferrous metal tools), and represents a revolutionary change in the history of man. For that reason it has been called the Neolithic or First Industrial Revolution. There are still some peoples today who subsist principally by agriculture, and who possess or possessed no domestic animals, as for example the Pueblo Indians of the Southwest, and many African tribes who rely upon their stock-raising pastoral neighbors for milk and meat.

Pastoral Peoples

The main economic dependence of these peoples is upon the domestication of animals for food and other purposes. In most of the oldest food-producing settlements investigated by archeologists in Asia, Europe, and North Africa, it has been found that, in addition to the cultivation of plant foods, animals were also bred for food. Such a basic industry is known as *mixed farming*. Mixed farming probably followed rapidly upon the discovery of agriculture. Sheep, goats, swine, and horned cattle were the principal food animals, and it will be noted that these are still the basic food animals, with the later addition of the fowl of contemporary man. Today, there are still many peoples who remain principally pastoralists. In America the Navaho Indians of the Southwest were originally pastoralists and mainly still are, although they have, during the last three hundred years, added agriculture, which they learned from the Pueblo Indians, to their subsistence economy. The Navaho word for corn means "enemy food," the food they learned to eat from their enemies the Pueblo Indians. The Bedouin of Saudi Arabia, the Kazak tribes of sheepherders of Central Asia, and many peoples of Central Asia, southwest Asia, North Africa, and the Middle East, still live chiefly by stockbreeding.

It is to be observed that there is a common principle underlying the production of plant and animal food, namely, the control of reproduction. And it is further to be observed that none of the categories of getting a living mentioned above are necessarily mutually exclusive. Some hunters do a little primitive agriculture. Agricultural peoples frequently domesticate food animals, and

Economic activities: pastoral, agricultural, hunting, and the preparation of food.

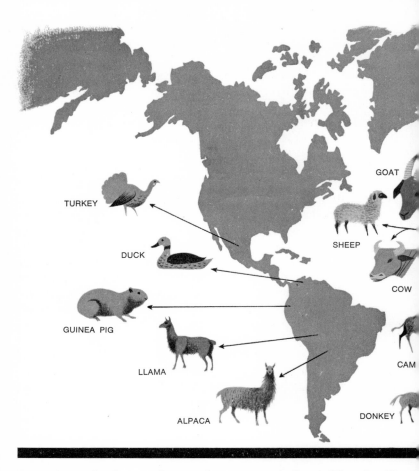

pastoral peoples frequently practice some agriculture. The classification above merely relates to the dominant food-producing practices of peoples.

Artisan and Urban Peoples

Specialization of occupations and residence in towns characterize these peoples. The transformation of small villages of self-sufficient farmers into teeming towns, occurred for the first time in the history of man some 9,000 years ago in the Middle East. The first such town of which we have any knowledge is Jericho, not the Biblical Jericho, but a much earlier one at the base of the same

106

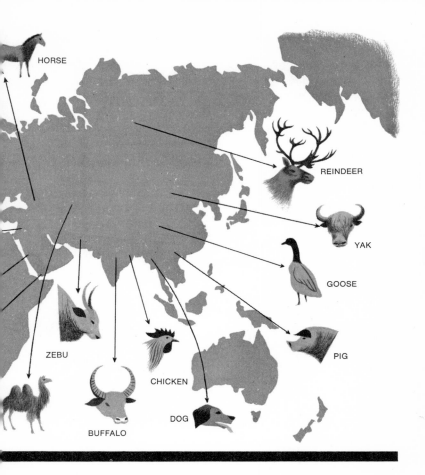

HORSE

REINDEER

YAK

GOOSE

PIG

ZEBU

CHICKEN

DOG

BUFFALO

Probable centers of origin of major domesticated animals.

site. This Neolithic town had all the attributes of civilization except that of pottery and a written language—civilization being characterized by the fact that the society is highly organized, artificialized, and increasingly removed from contact with nature. The town and civilization develop together. The region in which civilization was almost certainly born was in "the Fertile Crescent," the great area of land fringing the open deserts from Palestine to the Persian Gulf. This area was more particularly favorable for the cre-

The Fertile Crescent, the vast semicircle of land that fringes the great deserts from Palestine to the Persian Gulf. The birthplace of civilization.

ation of the first great towns and civilizations, for in this river valley the fertility of the alluvial soil, especially when artificially irrigated, was unsurpassed. Huge surpluses of food could be accumulated, and these could be traded for other goods. For while an alluvial soil may provide an abundance of foodstuffs, it is poor in those other materials essential to the pursuit of civilized life. It is

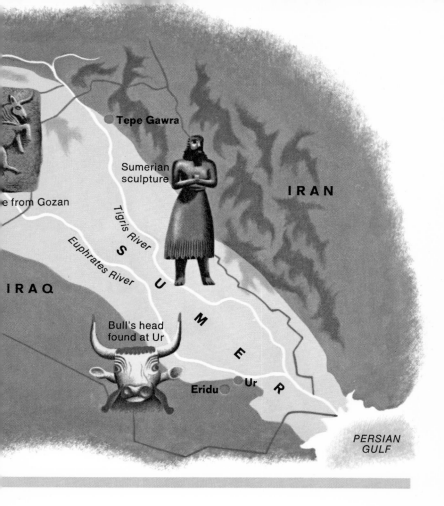

Tepe Gawra

Sumerian
sculpture

IRAN

e from Gozan

Tigris River

Euphrates River

S
U
M
E
R

IRAQ

Bull's head
found at Ur

Eridu

Ur

PERSIAN
GULF

in response to such challenges that the Sumerians became great
traders, and set up the first highly organized towns with a large
variety of different kinds of artisans, silversmiths, goldsmiths,
metal-workers, architects, builders and the like, priests, book-
keepers, overseers and overlords.

In a society with a strong sense of private property, literature,
religious and secular, can be preserved and transmitted by oral
tradition, but commercial transactions, especially when they come
to be conducted on an impersonal level, require something more

dependable than the retrospective falsification called memory. Hence it came about that it was in Sumer that writing was invented about 5,500 years ago. The progress from barbarism to civilization apparently requires three necessary conditions: (1) a complex social hierarchy (either royal or theocratic), (2) systematic urbanization, and (3) strong political control and adequate concentration of economic resources. These conditions appear to have come into being for the first time during the later centuries of the fourth millennium B.C., and then only in Sumer and Egypt, and subsequently in China, India, Greece, and in Middle America, to name but a few such societies. It is in the ability to transmit technical skills to successive generations that the foundations of civilization originate, for civilization is the extracorporeal, artificial, man-made part of the world which is the product of tool manufacture of increasing complexity in response to the enlarging concepts of community life evolving in the minds of men.

The urban revolution which occurred in Sumer has been called the Second Industrial Revolution and a major revolution in the history of man, indeed, it was. It liberated man from bondage to the tasks of food production and enabled the development of specialized occupations to be followed in more or less freedom, especially among the expert craftsmen. We see this sort of thing happening before our eyes in the kingdoms of Africa which for many hundreds of years have exhibited the transitions from the village to the town.

In the course of social evolution there has been a development which roughly follows the schema set out above, but this does not for a moment mean that every society has passed through each of these stages of development. Many societies have, but some have not. For example, many peoples of the Pacific have passed from a Stone Age culture directly into a full or marginally urbanized culture as a result of culture contact with urbanized peoples. *Acculturation* is the term applied to the processes which occur when two or more cultures come into durable direct contact. Acculturation is not to be confused with *diffusion*. Diffusion depends not so much on direct contact as upon transmission of cultural traits through intermediary communities. It is through the dual but independent processes of acculturation and diffusion that great cultural changes have been brought about in the societies affected by them. Many societies have been much affected by these processes, whereas others have been largely bypassed by their influence. In the historical reconstruction of the history of every society these factors must always be taken into consideration. Traits which may appear to be due to diffusion may, in fact, be due to independent invention. It is sometimes difficult to prove independent invention, and, indeed, the examples of independent invention which can be proved are few. They usually involve peoples who are reasonably well known and who have been isolated for considerable periods of time, so that it is unlikely that there could have been any intermediary contacts with other peoples for the transmission of the particular invention. Such are the invention of the symbol for zero independently by the Asiatic Indians and the Maya of Middle America, the independent invention of the cantilever-suspension bridge by non-Melanesian peoples and by the natives of New Guinea, the blowpipe gun shooting light darts tipped with poison in the Malay Peninsula and Amazon Valley. Agriculture, as we have seen, was probably independently discovered by several peoples, and no doubt there were a good many other independent discoveries, but it is very difficult to determine which were so.

Social Organization

Every society is organized to canalize the energy of its members in a manner that enables them to work together to achieve common ends. This gives each society its peculiar structure. Within that *social structure* there functions a network of social relations between individuals and between groups. The study of structurally prescribed relationships between individuals and between groups is the study of *social organization*. Social organization is the way in which the society is organized to function in the service of the individual and of the society. As such, social organization functions to preserve the individual and society; and as such, human nature is largely a function of the social organization in which it has been conditioned. Social structure stresses the expected relation between individuals; social organization stresses their actual relations.

Social organization begins in the arrangements which exist between the nurturing mother and her child, and the providing husband, and then goes on to the interactive relations which exist between all the members of a society. Interaction occurs not alone between individuals but between categories of individuals. Thus,

Wedding Scene. Sikkim.

my father is also the principal of my school; at home I act toward him in his status as my father, at school I act toward him in his status as principal. Mr. Jones is my friend, but he is also my commanding officer in the reserve. In short, an individual may occupy several positions in a society. Such a position is a *status*. *The status* of an individual represents the sum total of all his statuses. A status is a collection of rights and duties; in other words, it defines what one may expect from others and what others may expect from one's self. Status determines the limits and conditions of social relationships, but is not the same thing as those relationships. The dynamic aspect of status, the way in which the individual acts out his status, is his *role*.

Statuses are *ascribed* and *achieved*. Ascribed statuses are assigned to individuals regardless of innate abilities. By birth one acquires social class status, sexual status, and racial status. Achieved statuses are not assigned but are more or less filled through competition. It is through the whole range of statuses, which begin with the relations of children to their parents and terminate with one's relations to one's society, that the interactions beween individuals and between groups are largely organized by societies. Sexual status determines the position of sexes in relation to one another; age-grades determine the position of infants, children, adolescents, mature individuals and old-aged individuals to each other and to their social groups, and one's status in relation to one's relatives entails obligations of a very different nature from those expected by unrelated persons. This brings us very naturally to the matter of kinship.

Kinship

In every society biological and social relationships will serve to produce closer ties between some individuals than between others. The structured system of relationships which serve to bind individuals to one another as relatives is known as the *kinship system*. Methods of reckoning relationship differ very widely in various societies. In western societies like our own, in which the kinship system is based on biological relationships, we also recognize certain social relatives, that is relatives acquired through marriage. Such relatives are not *consanguineal relatives*, that is based in biological relationships, but are known as *affinal relatives*. In many societies the kinship system is based on social relationships rather than on biological ones. For example, in our society the father of a child is its biological father, but among the Australian aborigines the father of a child was the husband of the child's mother. The father might have been away for several years from his wife, but all the children born during his absence were considered to be his children. This was rationalized in an elaborate system of beliefs concerning the spirit origin of all children, and the belief that the mother is merely the incubator of the child, and that the father plays no physiological role in the conception of a child. Hence, both maternal and paternal relationship is socially determined even though those relationships have their origin in the nuclear family. The truth is that even in the nuclear family of the Western world the paternity of a child is an assumption, for no one, with the possible exception of the mother, can be quite certain that a particular man is the father of a particular child. The social contract is that the husband of the mother shall be *assumed* to be the biological father, except under conditions in which the husband declines to subscribe to this custom. It should be clearly understood that many men in Western societies assume full paternity of a child born to their wives who was biologically actually fathered by another man, without anyone other than husband and wife ever knowing. In nonliterate societies every child must have a recognized father. Children born out of wedlock are extremely rare in such societies, owing to the infecundity of the immature girl, and for the child who may be born to a woman in the absence of her husband, the conception of social paternity is sufficient to assure it a legitimate father, the husband of its mother. Of course, much more is involved in social paternity than an ascribed status, for the kinship of a father with his children is invested with and solidified by a vast ramifying and integrating network of relationships that bind parent and child together as firmly as any biologically conceived relationships could do. In nonliterate societies these relationships are considered to be perfectly natural, they are those of totemic membership (see page 122), clan (see page 121) and moiety (see page 122) relationship, and in these ways ancestral relationship. The reason why the birth of a child to an unmarried mother is condemned in nonliterate societies is not because it is considered immoral, but because the child has no socially accepted father and therefore creates a social situation for which there are no adequate arrangements.

Kinship relationships, however they may vary in different societies, are not due to accident, but are strictly related to the structure of the society. No society is a planless hodgepodge, a thing of shreds and patches. On the contrary, every cultural trait fits into the whole in a functionally related manner. Kinship relationships are no exception to this rule. They are found in every society to be functionally related to those cultural arrangements which the society has set up as the roles which individuals are to play in certain relationships to one another, their privileges, obligations, and expectations. It is not possible here to consider the varieties of relationship systems, as kinship systems may be called, but it should be clear that all kinship systems constitute an arrangement of functional relationships. These regulate the social relations between individuals and form, among other things, the basis upon which permanent unions leading to the birth of children may be contracted, that is, marriage.

Marriage

Marriage is the legal union between a man and woman as husband and wife entered into with the assumption of permanency. In all societies marriage is strictly regulated. One cannot, for example, marry relatives of certain kinds or at all in a good many societies. In many nonliterate societies one can only marry certain relatives or not at all. In many such societies one marries one's cross-cousin. *Cross-cousins* are individuals whose parents are brother and sister. As a male you will marry your mother's brother's daughter. As a female you will marry your father's sister's son. But among some other peoples, such as the Miwok of California and the Murngin of Australia, while it is permissible to marry the daughter of one's maternal uncle it is not permissible to marry the daughter of one's maternal aunt. Among the Trobriand Islanders, the reverse is true. Such forms of marriage are termed *asymmetrical cross-cousin marriages*. In some societies, in order to keep the males within the band, as among the Bedouin of northern Arabia, the marriage of a male tends to be with the daughter of his father's brother. This is known as *parallel-cousin marriage*. Among the Bedouin, the function of this form of marriage was to preserve a strong defensive fighting force.

Upon marriage the wife usually is required to live with her husband in his village, a custom known as *patrilocal* or *virilocal* residence. Occasionally the opposite custom prevails and the husband goes to live in his wife's village. This is known as *matrilocal* or *uxorilocal residence*. A frequent compromise is *matri-patrilocal* residence, in which matrilocal residence is required, usually for about one year, followed by permanent patrilocal residence. Where the married couple is required to assume residence near the maternal uncle of the groom the custom is termed *avunculocal* residence.

Patrilocal residence is associated with societies in which men come to supplant women as tillers of the soil, or follow pastoralism, or in hunting economies provide the major part of the subsistence. Among lower agricultural peoples in which women are the principal workers of the land, matrilocal residence and matrilineal descent are common. Matri-patrilocal residence becomes established as a supplement or partial supplement for the payment of the bride price.

In many societies it is compulsory to marry the widow of one's deceased brother. In other societies it is not obligatory but expected. Usually it is a younger brother who is expected to assume this obligation, for the older brothers are already likely to be married. This custom, very widely distributed, is known as the *levirate* (Latin: *levir*, brother-in-law). In other societies one is required to marry a younger sister of one's deceased wife. This custom is known as the *sororate*. The Chiricahua Apaches of North America, who practiced both the levirate and sororate, consider it "an intolerable insult" for a widower to look elsewhere than to his deceased wife's sisters or cousins for a second wife. In a number of African societies a man could inherit his father's widows with the exception of his own mother. Among the Omaha and Miwok Indians a man could marry his wife's brother's daughter, and an Omaha could also marry his wife's paternal aunt. Such marriages were desirable in a tribe where few females were available and it was necessary to maintain the numerical strength of the tribe. Some societies, for similar reasons, were widely permissive. The Tamanak of the Orinoco River, for example, permitted filial widow inheritance, the levirate, the sororate, marriage with the daughter of the wife's sister, with the sister's daughter, and symmetrical cross-cousin marriage.

Marriage prohibitions take a large variety of different forms, but marriage between parent and child is universally proscribed, and

Central Australian Aboriginal at spirit center inhabited by spirit babies.

between brother and sister also, except in the royal families of ancient Egypt, pre-Columbian Peru, and Hawaii where brother-sister marriage was the custom. In these exceptional instances the motivation for brother-sister marriage appears to have been the view that no one other than a member of one's immediate family was of pure enough blood to be worthy of marriage into the royal house. There was no horror of incest here. The prohibition against incest, that is against sexual intercourse between persons considered to be too closely related to marry legally, is based principally on social considerations and not on biological ones. In many societies the children of parallel uncles and aunts are called "brothers" and "sisters" by their cousins, and since they are regarded as close "blood" relatives, marriage between them is considered incestuous and is forbidden.

While most nonliterate peoples live in monogamous unions, that is in a marriage of only one person to another, there are generally no restrictions upon the number of wives a man may have. The opposite is not true, a woman may generally have but one husband no matter how many additional wives *he* may have. An exception to this rule is represented by the Toda of southern India. Among the Toda the dominant form of marriage is *polyandry*, that is, marriage of one woman to two or more men, generally brothers. Among the Toda, female infanticide was practiced. This resulted in very few females, hence the solution provided by polyandry. *Polygyny*, where one man may marry two or more women who serve as his wives, is a widespread custom, particularly in Africa. *Polygamy* refers to marriage to two or more husbands or wives, and when these are maintained simultaneously the custom may be referred to as *parallel polygamy*, in contrast to the *sequential polygamy*, which is practiced in some segments of western societies where by divorce one can sequentially enjoy a number of different spouses.

Divorce

Divorce is the legal dissolution of a legally recognized marriage. Among nonliterate peoples divorce is generally easily accomplished, so that it is not uncommon to find individuals in such societies who have been married several times. Lowie reports a contemporary Hopi woman who is known to have had eight official husbands. A young Greenland Eskimo woman described by Holm had just left her sixth husband. Among the Crow Indians a wife could be divorced for being "cranky." In our own society this would be called "incompatibility of temperament" or "mental cruelty." Barrenness is a common ground for divorce. Among the Toda, if the wife was considered stupid or would not work, she could be divorced. Adultery, on the other hand, in most nonliterate societies rarely constituted ground for divorce, and was not always even punished.

Divorce is not, as a rule, any more difficult for women than it is for men in nonliterate societies, and in some it is easier, as among

Temple of Athena Nike, Acropolis, Athens, 426 B.C.

the Kwomas of New Guinea, the Dahomeans of West Africa, the Yurok of California, and the Witoto of Brazil. In some societies, such as the Arunta of Australia and the Baganda of East Africa, while the male can divorce his wife at will the female has no such rights. In many other societies men and women enjoy equal rights of divorce. But in all nonliterate societies, in spite of the ease with which divorce can be obtained, it is not as frequent as might be supposed. Children hold husband and wife together and the mutual economic advantages conferred by each spouse upon one another, not to mention economic obligations which frequently arise from divorce, are sufficiently weighty considerations influencing the maintenance of the marriage.

The Family and the Group

The family is the association brought into being by the institution of marriage. There are four principal functions of the family: (1) sexual, (2) economic, (3) reproductive, and (4) educational.

Three kinds of family are recognized: (1) The *nuclear family*, (sometimes called the *biological* or *conjugal family*), consisting of husband and wife and their children. Through marriage each spouse in the nuclear family becomes a member of two families; the nuclear family is therefore *bilateral*. (2) The *polygamous family* consists of several nuclear families which are linked through a common spouse. For example, in polygynous unions one man is husband and father in several nuclear families, and as such united

119

them into a single polygamous family. In polyandrous unions one woman performs the same role, uniting a number of nuclear families into one polygamous family. (3) The *extended family* (or joint family) consists of two or more nuclear families affiliated by the extension downward from parent to child as contrasted with the bilateral extension of the husband-wife relationship in the nuclear family. The patriarchal family, presided over by the grandfather, which long prevailed in Europe, constitutes a good example of a patrilocal extended family. In nonliterate societies the extended family usually occupied a single large dwelling; its member families lived in adjacent smaller ones. When family relationships are treated unilaterally, and descent is reckoned and property descends in a single line, and the child is considered to belong to the extended family of its father, the rule is termed *patrilineal*; where the child is considered to belong to the extended family of the mother, the rule is termed *matrilineal*; where descent is reckoned equally in both the male and female lines or indifferently in either, the rule is known as *bilateral descent*; finally where the indi-

New Guinea masks.

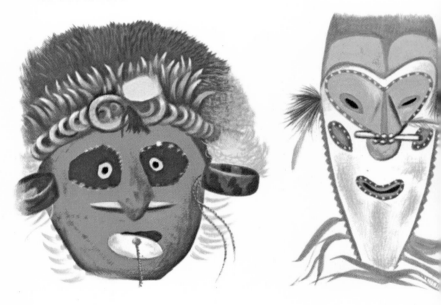

vidual may claim descent through affiliation both with paternal and maternal groups, the rule is termed *double descent*.

The Clan

As we have seen, rules of residence are closely related to general economic, social, and cultural conditions. Residence rules bring together in one locality a group of relatives with their families. Two major social groups arise out of such aggregations of relatives or kinsmen, *extended families* and *clans*. The extended family has already been discussed. A kinship group or sib (members of a common consanguineal group produced by unilinear descent) that traces its descent through the paternal or the maternal line, usually requiring marriage outside the kin-group, that is *exogamy*, is a *clan*. A *patriclan* is one in which, by patrilocal residence and patrilineal descent formed around its male members, a group results which includes all males and unmarried females of the patrilineal group; the married females of the *lineage* (that is, the consanguineal group who are not always able to trace genealogical relationships between individuals), the male's sisters, are excluded because they are resident in the patrilocal clans of their husbands. The reverse rules

obtain in the *matriclan*. Avunculocality produces the *avuncuclan*, consisting of matrilineally related uncles and nephews or of real or classificatory brothers, with their wives and children.

The clan serves as an auxiliary family, uniting the members in a common bond of kinship, privileges, and duties. It is not a group one can voluntarily join. The functions of the clan are principally: (1) to provide a bond of solidarity between its members through the belief in common descent, (2) to provide its members with all the necessary securities and protections they might otherwise lack, (3) to regulate and control marriage, (4) to adjudicate in disputes; and secondarily to provide the following sanctions for its members: (1) governmental, (2) economic, (3) religious and ceremonial, and (4) totemic.

Where sibs consider themselves in a purely conventional unilinear bond of kinship, more substantial than that which unites them to other sibs, such as a consanguineal group, it is called a *phratry* (Greek: *phrater*, brother). Societies in which there are only two sibs or phratries are called *moieties*. Moieties may be *exogamous*, that is, marrying outside the moiety, *agamous*, not regulating marriage, or *endogamous*, marriage within the group.

Totemism

A common characteristic of lineages, sibs, and moieties is *totemism*. A totem (an Ojibwa Indian word) is a plant, animal, natural object, or phenomenon to which the members of a kinship group individually and in common consider themselves to be related in some special way. Members of totemic groups are usually exogamic, and their totemic membership serves not only to relate them closely to other members but to the world of nature as represented by the totem. Respect for one's own totem and that of others is universal. One does not generally eat the plant or animal which is one's totem or one eats sparingly of it or only on ceremonial occasions, though one may eat, without offense, the totemic plants or animals of others.

Religion

Every people of which we have a record has been characterized by adherence to some religion. Religion, like marriage and the family, is a cultural universal. What is religion? Edward Burnett

Tylor's minimum definition, "the belief in spiritual beings," given in his *Primitive Culture*, 1871, is as sound as it ever was. All peoples make some distinction between the secular, everyday, ordinary, natural world and the sacred, transcendent, extraordinary, supernatural world. It is the emotions, ideas, attitudes, beliefs, and acts dedicated to the supernatural, to the belief in spiritual beings, that constitute religion.

It may be noted that no reference has been made to a belief in a supreme being or beings. This omission is not accidental, for the fact is that there are quite a number of peoples who do not believe in a supreme being, as for example, the Wintun Indians of north-central California, the Bushmen, most Australian aboriginal peoples, and most Eskimo peoples. It will be noted at once that all these peoples are food-gathering-hunting peoples, and there is, indeed, a striking correlation between a people's economic organization and the kind of spiritual beings in which it believes. It has been suggested that this is due not so much to the methods of food production as to the development of a priestly class which finds it to its advantage to elaborate the notion of a supernatural or supreme being. Where agriculture exists but caste and class distinctions are scarcely or only slightly developed, as through the whole of Melanesia and in many parts of North and South America, with few exceptions the belief in true gods or deities is not to be found. A true god or deity has a very definite and fixed character. The spirit beings of food-gathering-hunting societies are anything but that. They are generally lacking in sharp characterization and are more often than not quite inconsistently defined. For example, the Arunta of Australia believe that the world was created by two formless beings, whom they call *Numbakulla*, that is, self-existing beings. They came out of nothing and originally existed in the western sky, but they long ago ceased to be. Thus, the spirit beings who created the Australian Arunta and their world not only had no form but don't even any longer exist! This is more like a philosophical concept or evolutionary theory than a religious belief.

In every nonliterate society the medicine man or shaman is by temperament, training, and vocation, the individual who is believed to be possessed of powers which enable him to communicate with and manipulate the supernaturals. Since in most nonliterate societies religion is essentially a practical matter, a means of in-

New Guinea medicine man with spirit flute.

creasing the food supply by the celebration of the proper rituals, of obtaining security, even wealth, the shaman would be too much occupied with the practice of his trade to have time for the formulation of any ideas of a supreme being. The shaman was more often than not a highly neurotic person, and his behavioral abnormalities only served to add to his other-worldly character. When he died or rather departed for the other world, his ghost could very readily become the mold for a supernatural spirit. It was not the shaman himself who was spiritualized but the spiritual essence which he represented.

It is when we pass from the food-gathering-hunter peoples to reach the agricultural peoples that the idea of a supreme being begins to make its appearance, bearing all the marks of a specially privileged priestly class and group. This class usually possesses a certain economic and social dominance, and the evidence indicates that it is from this class that the belief in a supreme being originated. For example, among the Dakota and Winnebago Indians, among the Polynesians, and in West Africa the belief in a supreme being is recognized as the private and specific belief of the priests, and is so acknowledged by the priests themselves.

There are a number of simpler nonliterate cultures that possess a belief in a supreme being, but this belief is rather more of a philosophical than of a religious nature because no ritual is connected with his worship. He is not associated with creation myths, prayers are not addressed to him, and he has no direct relation to the world. In these cultures, the two traits always ascribed to the supreme being are that he is good and righteous. Nonliterate peoples having such a supreme being are the southeastern Australians, the Andaman Islanders, the Negritos of the Philippine Islands, and the Selknam of Tierra del Fuego.

The belief in a single supreme deity, that is, *monotheism*, is extremely rare. Monotheism is to be distinguished from *monolatry*, the belief in one supreme being where others are also acknowledged to exist; thus monolatry is essentially a form of *polytheism*, the belief in many gods.

The supreme being of the more sophisticated cultures is characterized by creativeness, omnipotence, omnipresence, immortality, unalterable goodness, and righteousness. Such a conception of a supreme being is rare among nonliterates and is to be found mostly among the more highly developed societies.

Theories Concerning the Origin of Religion

There are many theories concerning the origin of religion. Herbert Spencer (1820-1903), the English sociologist, believed that it arose out of ancestor worship. Sir James Frazer (1854-1941), the English anthropologist, thought that it developed out of magic. Emile Durkheim (1858-1917), the French sociologist, thought that the religious feeling was the outcome of group excitement, the elevation of feeling (euphoria) which one experiences when the members of the tribe come together in joint celebration. Religion is ultimately, therefore, the most primitive of all social phenomena, and it is indeed, according to Durkheim, society. Edward Burnett Tylor (1832-1917), the English anthropologist, saw the origin of religion in *animism*, in the beliefs about souls of individual creatures capable of existence after death, and of other spirits up to the rank of powerful deities. *Animism* is the belief in the animation of living things by spirits. Paul Radin (1883-1959), American anthropologist, has realistically argued for a multiple and complex origin for religious phenomena, in which the priestly formulator plays a considerable role. Others have argued for a pre-animistic origin of religion brought about in the interplay of the emotions of awe, fear and wonder at the supernatural. Still others have derived religion from mystic experience, while some have considered religion to have developed as a normal psychological adjustment by which societies have built a protective barrier of fantasy against fear.

All these theories are, of course, conjectural. Even the very origin of the word "religion" is debatable, the most popular etymology being the Latin *religare*, "to bind together." Whatever the origin of the word, *religare* certainly suggests one of the dominant characteristics of the religious feeling and a principal function of religion: the binding of men to their fellow men and to the world of which they are all part, this world and the other world of the supernatural.

The World of Supernatural Power

Many nonliterate peoples believe that the universe is charged with a wonderful supernatural power. That power, first described by Bishop Codrington in 1891 as a widespread belief among the Melanesians of the Pacific, is "a force altogether distinct from physical power which acts in all kinds of ways for good and evil and which it is of the greatest advantage to possess and control. This supernatural power is called *mana*. It is in some ways akin to our concept of "luck," or what the Greeks called the aleatory element. *Mana* just works of itself. In Melanesia it is largely regarded as an impersonal force; objects possess it but not men. Men can acquire it by taking possession of some object rich in *mana*. As one Fiji Islander put it, "A thing has *mana* when it works; it has no *mana* when it does not work." *Mana* is the supernatural essence which is responsible for everything beyond the power of men, and it is something that works beyond the common processes of nature. It is not possessed by persons, though it may attach itself to them. The Polynesian conception of *mana* differed to the extent that it could be an inherent quality of persons of high rank. In Polynesia the distribution of *mana* followed strictly along class lines. Kings and chiefs and nobility had the greatest amount, commoners least, and women less than men. *Mana*, in Polynesia, could also be dangerous to those who possessed little of it and had the misfortune to come into contact, even at a remove, with one possessing much. Thus, in Polynesia the idea of *mana* was associated with a highly elaborate complex of *taboos*, that is, prohibitions and avoidance regulations designed to protect the individual against the dangerous effects of *mana*.

Similar concepts of supernatural power are found in many parts of the world. Among North American Indians the belief was very common. The Algonquin-speaking tribes, mainly living in the area north and east of the central Great Plains, spoke of *manitou*, which embraced all supernatural power both personal and impersonal. The Siouan *wakan* and the Iroquois *orenda* have essentially the same meaning. A similar concept was the aboriginal Japanese *Kami*, which persisted into modern times. *Kami* is a quality with which supernatural beings, rulers, members of royal lineages, remarkably shaped stones, trees, waterfalls, and mountains, were all invested. Ordinary human beings could have no *kami*.

That such conceptions of the supernatural are closely related to religious beliefs is evident. While *animism* requires an active entering into relation with spiritual beings, the belief in mana (using that term as roughly equvalent for all such beliefs) is of another kind, for mana is powerful of itself and affects the lives of men regardless of anything they can do about it. When the nonliterate behaves toward inanimate objects as if they were animate we speak of *animatism*. In animatism the individual does not necessarily attribute any supernatural quality to the object, but simply considers that it has the power to do what he believes it capable of doing.

ARCHEOLOGICAL TIME CHART

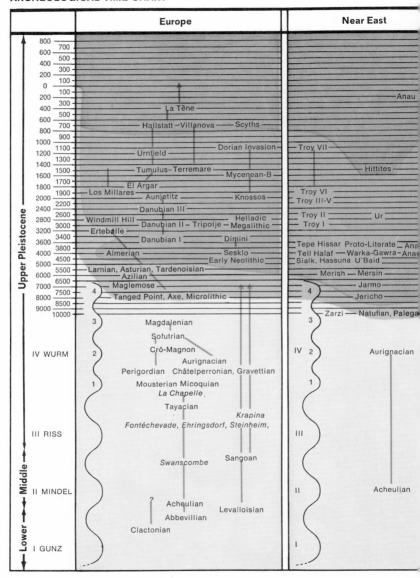

Italicized names refer to fossil hominid forms. Names in Roman refer to Industries and/or Perio◄

The wavy ascending lines indicate variations in climatic conditions. The convexities toward th￼ right-hand side of the page indicating the colder periods, the concavities the warmer period◄ The numbers at the upper parts of the wavy line indicate the four *interstadials* or cool-ten￼ perate periods.

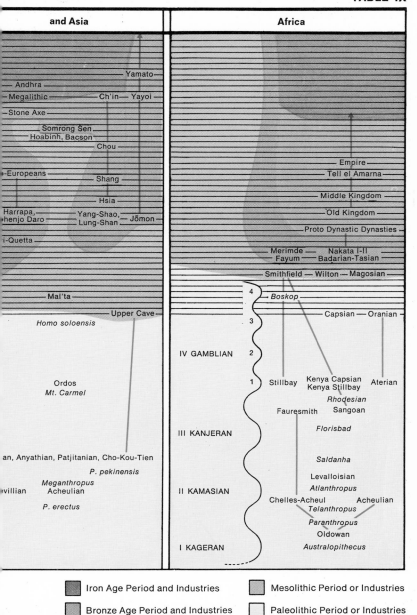

TABLE IX

and Asia	Africa

Yamato

Andhra

Megalithic — Ch'in — Yayoi

Stone Axe

Somrong Sen
Hoabinh, Bacson
Chou

Empire

Tell el Amarna

Europeans — Shang

Middle Kingdom

Hsia

Old Kingdom

Harrapa,
henjo Daro — Yang-Shao,
Lung-Shan — Jōmon

Proto Dynastic Dynasties

i-Quetta

Merimde — Nakata I-II
Fayum — Badarian-Tasian

Smithfield — Wilton — Magosian

Mal'ta

4 — *Boskop*

Upper Cave

Capsian — Oranian

Homo soloensis

3

IV GAMBLIAN 2

1 Stillbay — Kenya Capsian
Kenya Stillbay — Aterian

Ordos
Mt. Carmel

Rhodesian

Fauresmith — Sangoan

III KANJERAN

Florisbad

an, Anyathian, Patjitanian, Cho-Kou-Tien

Saldanha

P. pekinensis

Levalloisian

Meganthropus
villian   Acheulian

Atlanthropus

II KAMASIAN   Chelles-Acheul — Acheulian

P. erectus

Telanthropus

Paranthropus

Oldowan

I KAGERAN   *Australopithecus*

■	Iron Age Period and Industries	■	Mesolithic Period or Industries
■	Bronze Age Period and Industries	■	Paleolithic Period or Industries
■	Neolithic Period or Industries		

Mana, animism, and animatism are not in essence religious phenomena, though from the standpoint of the study of the development of religion they are of the greatest interest. They are only potentially religious phenomena, becoming actually so when they are invested with religious emotional values. Such emotional religious values would be their relation to a deity, of worship, prayer, supplication of the supernatural, and the like.

Magic

Magic is a technique of coercing the supernatural to do one's bidding. Magic may be the special skill of medicine-men or specified others, or it may be a technique which anyone can practice, provided the traditional rules are followed. As a rite and a verbal formula directed toward the achievement of practical ends magic has three primary purposes: (1) productive, (2) protective, and (3) destructive. By magic one can influence the successful outcome of the hunt, of food supply, rain, of love, and the like. One can also avert misfortune, cure sickness, nullify the magic of one's enemies, taboo property, and so on. Finally, one can produce damage to the crops of one's enemies, destroy their property, cause them to fall ill, and even die.

It is to be observed that in all these claims for the effects of magic there is nothing essentially unreasonable. By magic one cannot convert oneself into a god, nor can one turn one's enemies into pigs. The causes produce not supernatural or miraculous, but natural effects. One uses certain things (instruments or medicines), utters certain words (the spell) and performs a certain rite, and if the conditions under which all these things have been done are the appropriate ones, the effect will naturally follow. If it doesn't, something has obviously not been right. Magic usually works, if not all the time certainly a great deal of the time. It produces visible results. When it doesn't, it is either due to some fault in the technique or to the countermagic of a sorcerer or witch.

Magic serves to give the nonliterate confidence in his enterprises and thus serves the important function of sustaining him under conditions which, in the absence of magic, would have the opposite effect. Magic gives the nonliterate the sense of power over the natural world, a control which he can exercise or have exercised for him, and which therefore leaves him not at the mercy of nature but virtually at its helm. It is a good feeling, and it works. No one can tell him that it doesn't.

Although magic as such is to be distinguished from religion as such, magic is a technique of religion and is often so intertwined with religious processes that in nonliterate and even in some literate societies one may properly speak of magico-religious beliefs. Magic is a way of coercing the supernatural. Magic is a substrate of religion, and one may readily perceive the nature of the contribution it makes to religion, for it proves the existence of the supernatural by the results it obtains.

It has been said that supernaturalism is the sole concern of magic, but the fact is that while much of magic is concerned with the supernatural, a good deal of it is directed toward the control of natural processes by what appears to be nonliterate man's science, since unlike other techniques in the magico-religious realm it is concerned with cause and effect sequences. The criteria of religion, involving submission, petition, conciliation, and consecration, are either wanting or not sharply drawn. Knowing the rules, and following them in detail, is sufficient to secure the desired effect. Frazer saw in the mental operations of the magician and the scientist an essential likeness and, indeed, wrote of the nonliterate magician as a primitive scientist. But this is to confuse things. In science there is no room for supernaturalism, and in his secular everyday life, the nonliterate uses scientific principles in the building of his outrigger canoes, in his agricultural processes, and in many other ways. Magic is not unrelated to science, but it is not science in any form. Frazer thought that an age of magic preceded an age of religion, but for this view of ages of magic and ages of religion there is no support whatever. Magic and religion are everywhere pursued as parallel activities, and they are often closely interrelated, but there is no evidence or ground for supposing that one ever preceded the other.

Mythology, Philosophy, and Science

A very evident and important trait of nonliterate cultures is the myth. Myths are traditional stories, accepted as historical, embodying the beliefs of a people concerning its creation, its gods, the universe, life and death. Myths, religious beliefs, and beliefs and experiences in connection with the belief in spirits and the supernatural all form parts of the same subject. The myth expresses, enhances, and codifies belief; it tends to safeguard and enforce morality; it testifies to the efficacy of ritual, and provides guidance for the life of man. Myth is not an idle tale or an intellectual explanation, but a well-tried and socially active force, a working charter of faith and wisdom. Among other things myths help to reconcile seemingly irreconcilables and contradictions in the individual's view of the world and what he has deduced from experience. Myths help to make the world more intelligible, and since it gives meaning to many seemingly unconnected events, and connects them, it has a high organizing value. Without a mythology the world remains merely phenomenal, chaotic, and fragmentary. It is the very chaos of experience which evokes man's myth-making activities in the attempt to bring order to what would otherwise remain disordered, to unify what would remain disassociated.

Myths are to be distinguished from folk tales by the fact that myths refer to events or things believed to have taken place in the remote past, whereas folk tales represent a people's unrecorded traditions as they appear in its customs, beliefs, magic, and ritual.

Philosophy

Respect for knowledge and wisdom, and concern with the processes of thought and conduct, are found among individuals in most nonliterate cultures. The conception of "primitive man" beridden with fear, overwhelmed by superstition, incapable of thinking for himself, and utterly credulous, is a stereotype which may apply to some nonliterates, just as it may apply to millions of persons living in literate cultures, but it does grave injustice to the many fine minds that are encountered in both cultures. Not everyone is a philosopher or thinker in nonliterate societies, any more than everyone is so in literate societies. What is surprising to those unacquainted with nonliterate peoples is the extraordinary critical faculty that some nonliterate thinkers exhibit. Such thinkers in nonliterate societies attempt to discover what there is in an effect, how it came about, what the true relations are between things. In 1927 Professor Paul Radin published a fascinating book, *Primitive Man as a Philosopher*, in which for the first time he brought to-

Cherokee alphabet, invented by an American Indian, Sequoya, and published in 1821.

Cherokee Alphabet.

D a	R e	T i	Ꭷ o	O u	i v
S ga Ꭴ ka	F ge	Y gi	A go	J gu	E gv
Ꮣ ha	Ꭾ he	Ꭿ hi	Ꮙ ho	Ꮁ hu	Ꮗ hv
W la	Ꮄ le	Ꮅ li	G lo	M lu	Ꮑ lv
Ꮉ ma	Ꭳ me	H mi	Ꮀ mo	Y mu	
Ꭴ na Ꮕna Gnah	Ꮄ ne	Ꮏ ni	Z no	Ꮠ nu	Ꮕ nv
Ꮖ qua	Ꮗ que	Ꮘ qui	Ꮚ quo	Ꮜ quu	Ꮝ quv
Ꮖ sa Ꮼs	Ꮞ se	Ꮟ si	Ꮠ so	Ꮡ su	R sv
Ꮪ da Ꮤ ta	Ꮫ de Ꮦ te	Ꮧ di Ꮨ ti	Ꮩ do	S du	Ꮫ dv
Ꮪ dla Ꮬ tla	Ꮭ tle	C tli	Ꮯ tlo	Ꮰ tlu	P tlv
Ꮳ tsa	Ꮴ tse	Ꮵ tsi	Ꮶ tso	Ꮷ tsu	Ꮸ tsv
Ꮹ wa	Ꮺ we	Ꮻ wi	Ꮼ wo	Ꮽ wu	6 wv
Ꮿ ya	Ᏸ ye	Ᏹ yi	Ᏺ yo	Ᏻ yu	Ᏼ yv

Sounds represented by Vowels

a, as a in father, or short as a in rival.   o, as aw in law, or short as o in not.
e, as a in hate, or short as e in met.   u, as oo in fool, or short as u in pull.
i, as i in pique, or short as i in pit   v, as u in but, nasalized.

Consonant Sounds

g nearly as in English, but approaching to k. d nearly as in English but approaching to t. h.k.l.m.n.q.s.t.w.y. as in English. Syllables beginning with g. except Ꭶ have sometimes the power of k.A.S.Ꮩ are sometimes sounded to, tu, ti; and Syllables written with tl except Ꮮ sometimes vary to dl.

gether some of the evidence bearing testimony to the acuity of mind of many nonliterates. The widespread idea that "the savage" is a benighted heathen, stupid and unthinking, requires correction, and so does the notion that he is ethically undeveloped and ignoble in spirit, for the reverse is more likely than not to be true. The anthropological literature as well as much travel literature is replete with examples of the beauty of character, high ethical development, and nobility of thought characterizing many nonliterate peoples. Listen, for example, to Admiral Robert E. Peary on the Eskimos of West Coast Greenland: "They are savages, but they are not savage; they are without government, but they are not lawless; they are utterly uneducated according to our standard, yet they exhibit a remarkable degree of intelligence. In temperament like children, with all a child's delight in little things, they are nevertheless enduring as the most mature of civilized men and women, and the best of them are faithful unto death. Without religion and having no idea of God, they will share their last meal with anyone who is hungry, while the aged and the helpless among them are taken care of as a matter of course. They are healthy and pure-blooded; they have no vices, no intoxicants, and no bad habits —not even gambling. Altogether they are a people unique upon the face of the earth. A friend of mine well calls them the philosophic anarchists of the north. . . . To Christianize them would be quite impossible, but the cardinal graces of faith, hope, and charity they seem to have already, for without them they would never survive the six-months' night and the many rigors of their home." (*The North Pole*, New York, Macmillan, 1910, pp. 46-48.)

What Admiral Peary wrote of the Eskimo has innumerable times been confirmed of them and of numerous other nonliterate peoples. Among these the Australian aborigines and the Bushmen are outstanding examples, both of them food-gathering-hunting peoples, a "happenstance" which is no accident. If they are to survive, peoples living under such rigorous conditions must—as Admiral Peary pointed out for the Eskimo—live in complete co-operation with one another. It is true that under conditions of famine the aged and infirm will sometimes be abandoned, frequently at their own request, for under such conditions members of the group who cannot shift for themselves endanger the survival of all. This is the traditional understanding, and accepted by everyone, for these people have learned to endure, with unself-conscious dignity, the irremediable human condition.

The underlying ideals of conduct of most nonliterate peoples are self-discipline, self-control, and a determined endeavor to observe a proper measure of proportion in all things. Here are some statements made to Radin by the Winnebago Indians of Wisconsin and Nebraska which illustrate these points:

It is always good to be good. What does life consist of but love? Never do any wrong to children. Marry only one person at a time. It is not good to gamble. If you have a home of your own, see to it that whoever enters obtains something to eat. If you meet anyone on the road, even if it is only a child, speak a cheering word before you pass on. As you travel along life's road, never harm anyone or cause anyone to feel sad. On the contrary, if at any time you can make a person feel happy, do so. For the good you do everyone will love you. Of what value is it to kill? You ought to be of help to your fellow man. Do not abuse your wife; women are sacred. If you see a helpless old man, help him if you have anything at all. Be on friendly terms with everyone, and then everyone will love you. Do not imagine that you are taking your children's part if you just speak about loving them. Let them see it for themselves. Never think a home is yours until you have made one for yourself.

As Radin points out, among nonliterate peoples ethics is based upon behavior. The mere declaration of an ethical idea is not enough. Every ethical precept must be measured by the conduct of an individual. It is not enough to say that you believe; what is important is that you do what you say you believe.

The enjoyment of speculation and thinking for its own sake among nonliterates is a vast subject. Only a few examples can be given here. Here is an Oglala Dakota Indian:

"All living creatures and all plants derive their life from the sun. If it were not for the sun, there would be darkness and nothing could grow—the earth would be without life. Yet the sun must have the help of the earth. If the sun alone were to act upon animals and plants, the heat would be so great that they would die, but there are clouds that bring rain, and the action of the sun and earth together supply the moisture that is needed for life. The roots of a plant go down, and the deeper they go the more moisture

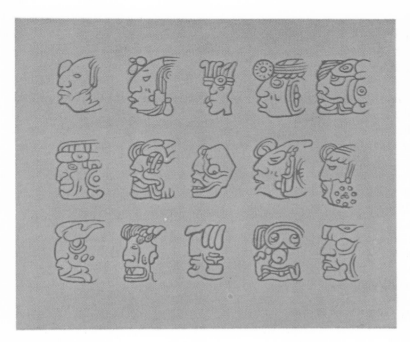

Mayan numerals from zero to fourteen.

they find. . . . From my boyhood I have observed leaves, trees, and grass, and I have never found two alike. They may have a general likeness, but on examination I have found that they differ slightly. Plants are of different families, each being adapted to growth in a certain locality. It is the same with animals; they are widely scattered, and yet each will be found in the environment to which it is best adapted. It is the same with human beings; there is some place which is best adapted to each. . . . An animal depends a great deal on the natural conditions around it. If the buffalo were here today, I think they would be different from the buffalo of the old days because all the natural conditions have changed. They would not find the same food nor the same surroundings. We see the change in our ponies. In the old days they could stand great hardship and travel long distances without water. They lived on certain kinds of food and drank pure water. Now our horses require a mixture of food; they have less endurance and must have constant care. It is the same with the Indians; they have less freedom and they fall an easy prey to disease. In the old days they were rugged and healthy, drinking pure water and eating the meat of the buffalo, which had a wide range, not being shut up like cattle of the present day."

And there was much else of a similar high order of reasoning. Skeptics and critics are not wanting in nonliterate societies, as is illustrated, for example, by the Maori who insisted that the gods died unless there were priests to keep them alive, or the Amazulu of East Africa who remarked of the supreme deity Unkulunkulu, that the old men claimed that he came out of a bed of reeds and gave being to man. "We children ask, where is the bed of reeds out of which Unkulunkulu came? . . . They say they speak the truth in saying there is a bed of reeds. But we say there is no bed of reeds, for we do not know the land in which it is, of which they can say it is in such and such a country." It was Tennyson who wrote, "There lies more faith in honest doubt, believe me, than in all your creeds." It is a point of view shared by more than one nonliterate thinker.

Nonliterate peoples generally have great respect for freedom of thought and expression as long as this is kept within the bounds of good taste. The average man in nonliterate societies, like the average man in literate societies, is likely to adhere to the conventions of thought and conduct, but he is rather more likely to be tolerant of unconventional views and conduct than is his literate counterpart. The same tolerance is extended to children who, on the whole, receive a great deal more respect than they do in literate societies, for nonliterates really believe that the child is father to the man.

In keeping with widespread misconceptions concerning the intellectual and critical abilities of nonliterate peoples is the notion that scientific processes of thought are entirely foreign to them. This is quite as false an idea as are most of the others that are held by "civilized" peoples about "primitive" peoples.

Both in science, which is systematized knowledge or a system of facts and principles, and technology, which is applied science, every nonliterate people has substantial achievements to its credit. Invention, that is origination by experiment, can be illustrated by innumerable examples drawn from nonliterate cultures. The outrigger canoe and the canoe itself are basic inventions, that is they involve the application of a new principle or combination of principles to the solution of an old problem. The Australian returning boomerang is another example of a basic invention. Inventions, of course, come about as a result of the pressure of necessity. Where there is no necessity there is no invention. Skis, snowshoes, sledrunners, the harnessing of dogs to draw sleds, metal-smelting, innumerable original ways of fishing, the setting of traps, the building of weirs, and much else, are all examples of independent invention by nonliterate peoples. Rubber and the drug curare were discovered by Central American Indians, and it was Sequoyah, a nonliterate Cherokee Indian who, singlehandedly, invented an entirely new alphabet which virtually enabled his people to learn to read and write overnight. And it was nonliterate Middle American Indians who created the highly literate Maya civilization of Yucatán, remarkable for its glyph writing, for its mathematics, its extraordinarily accurate calendar, its astronomy, its astonishing architectural accomplishments, metal work, sculpture, cities, and its social organization. Quite as remarkable in many ways were the Incas of Peru and the Aztecs of Mexico.

Science for the sake of science is seldom possible for nonliterates. For one thing there is the want of leisure, and for another, scientific processes of mind must be applied for purely practical ends. That nonliterate individuals are capable of the most careful observation, experiment, and application of their findings is abundantly testified to by their actual achievements.

Social Control, Government, and Law

The complex of interrelations that exists between the members of a group constitutes society. We have already considered some of the means by which the interrelations of human beings in society are organized. There remain to be considered such other forms of social control and organization as mores or folkways, government, political forms, and the law.

Mores, Folkways, or Custom

The moral standards of a group considered indispensable to its welfare are its *mores* (singular, *mos*). The popular habits or unwitting uniformities of behavior which arise in every society, become standardized, and have some degree of traditional sanction, such as handshaking, manner of dress, forms of eating, and the like, are *folkways*. Custom is generally used as a synonym of folk-ways and may be defined as the way of acting in defined situations that is of relatively long duration and is generally observed without deliberation. *Morals* consist of the mores and customs of the group, the rules of conduct which the group defines as right and which it imposes upon the individual by sanctions and penalties. Morals should not be confused with ethical standards or ideals, which may vary considerably from the prevailing moral standards or code. Ethical standards such as the injunction to love one's neighbor have neither sanctions nor penalties attached to them for their nonperformance, nor do ideals. But in every society the ethical man, and the man who attempts to realize his ideals, is honored and respected. Sometimes the distinction between morals, ethics, and ideal behavior is difficult or impossible to make, but that there is a distinction needs to be remarked.

In nonliterate societies the conduct of the individual insofar as it affects the welfare of the group is subject to his own self-discipline, and in general the member of a nonliterate society tends to regulate his conduct by his consciousness of his responsibility to the group. Group-consciousness is very much more of an immediate experience to the nonliterate because, among other things, the group is likely to be small and his interrelations with his fellows very much more direct and consequential than is the case for his opposite number in large literate societies. The enforcement of negative sanctions or penalties is also likely to be much more immediate than it is in literate societies.

Social recognition and appreciation by their fellow men is the kind of approval all men desire. It is for this reason that public opinion, the expression of the moral judgment of the group, is in all societies so effective an agency of social control. Quite often public opinion is no more than a complex of prejudices, sentiments, emotions, and conventions. Nevertheless, it constitutes a powerful means of control in all societies, for the individual cannot escape the judgment of his fellow men.

Government

In the development and control of social institutions and forces, the key institution is government. Government implies the authoritative administration of public affairs, and in most societies it is achieved principally through political forms and judicial and legal

Detail from cave painting at Lascaux (Dordogne), showing bird-headed man falling before wounded bison. The bird beneath may be a totemic emblem.

procedures. In nonliterate societies government constitutes the complex of institutions which serves to hold the community together, safeguarding its food supply and maintaining peace within and outside its borders. The two foundations upon which government or governmental-like principles rest in nonliterate societies are first the territorial principle, that is the territory belonging to the tribe; and second, the group principle, the group larger than the family, the local group, the clan, tribe or people. The disposition of the land, trespassing, and the food supply are problems of the community as a whole. The family constitutes the source of the earliest form of government, the head of the household being the principal governing authority, but in speaking of government the reference is always to the government of the community. An associated group of families, the *band*, provides the first occasion for government of the group. Among food-gathering-hunting peoples government is invariably constituted by a council of wise men, who come together when necessity demands.

Government serves as a means of channeling collective action and social control, and this justifies it to the governed. It is, how-

140

ever, only with settlement in villages or towns that government becomes a politically developed institution.

Independent communities may be organized as a common political entity having a common government; such an entity is a *state*. States obviously do not develop until societies have achieved both size and advancement, but they occur in many nonliterate societies of Africa. In North America a good example of a state was the Iroquois League of Nations, the federation known as "The Five Nations," consisting of the Mohawk, Oneida, Onondaga, Cayuga, and Seneca.

Five forms of government are recognized:

1. Theocracy—government by supernatural direction, through priest or other sacred agents.
2. Gerontocracy—government by old men.
3. Oligarchy—exclusive power vested in the hands of a small exclusive class.
4. Democracy—supreme power vested in the people and exercised by them directly or indirectly.
5. Monarchy—supreme power vested in the person of a king.

Law

Law is a formalized means of social control. A law is a rule of conduct imposed by authority with community sanction to apply physical force in the maintenance and punishment for the breaking of the law. *The* law is the codified (unwritten or written) body

of sanctions which prescribes the measures to be taken in enforcing the conduct deemed essential for the stability of society.

In the food-gathering-hunting societies the force of public opinion, sometimes reinforced by physical force or some other penalty, generally determined in council, serves to administer the law.

Laws are definitions of desired behavior, and as they progress societies usually come to recognize these forms of desired behavior as having the force of law, and such forms of behavior are eventually thus codified. While there are certain universally desired forms of behavior, there is considerable variability among the societies of the world in what is considered desirable conduct under certain conditions. Hence, what may be considered a crime in one society may at most be considered a misdemeanor in another. A *crime* is a wrong committed against the community, but a single murder is

Polychrome painting of bison, on wall of cave at Font-de-Gaume (France); and presumed engraved sketch for same on limestone, found 200 miles away at Genière near Serrières-sur-Aïn.

not so considered among the Eskimo, and it is a matter for private settlement rather than group action. On the other hand, selfishness is regarded as a crime among the Eskimo and punished as such, whereas in other societies it is regarded as no more than a regrettable trait.

Clearly the law, like every other social institution, bears an integral functional relation to the structure of the society of which it is a part, the law being adapted to meet the conditions that every society sets it in terms of its own needs.

Judicial Procedures

Judicial processes are treated with great seriousness and solemnity among most nonliterate peoples at every stage of development. At the simpler stages of cultural development there are no formally appointed judges or courts, and the people as a whole tend to act as judges. But even among food-gathering-hunting peoples, the council will meet to consider the evidence and hand down judgment. It requires to be said that such judgments of which we have a record testify to the profound understanding that nonliterate peoples have of the meaning of justice.

Trial by jury in Europe is a tenth century A.D. invention, but the council of nonliterate societies often constituted both judge and jury, and it was a majority judgment among the members of the council which decided the verdict.

The Arts

The languages of the imagination, drawing, painting, carving, sculpture, music, poetry, storytelling, and the dance, all find a place in virtually every society, however simple.

Through the discovery of prehistoric art during the latter part of the last century and the discovery of "primitive art" in this century, the extraordinary artistic abilities of nonliterate peoples have at last begun to be recognized. By virtue of the closeness with which they pay attention to their environment, nonliterate peoples generally develop acutely sharpened abilities which may lie in abeyance till they are called upon. This has occurred more than once to the astonishment of all who have witnessed it. Australian aboriginal children, for example, or adults, when initiated into European styles of drawing and painting, have turned in the most

143

astonishing artistic performances.

The important lesson we have learned from such performances is that the stylized art of a people should never constitute a basis upon which to judge its artistic capabilities in terms of another people's culture. From the stylized art of Australian aborigines it had, in fact, been reasoned by a large number of observers that they were incapable of anything so "advanced" as art in a "civilized" style. Never was there a less sound conclusion, and never was there one more resoundingly demonstrated, by the aborigines themselves, to be untrue. The art of prehistoric man, in mural, sculpture, and artifacts, speaks for itself.

The range of artistic ability exhibited by nonliterate peoples is astonishingly impressive, and far from being "primitive" it is in many cases highly sophisticated, indeed, much more so than much of the naturalistic art which was the prevailing style in the Western world up to the age of the impressionists. No one who has ever seen the bronze and terracotta heads made by Nigerian Ifé artists of the thirteenth century or Nigerian Benin bronzes and ivory masks can have any doubt that the naturalistic skill shown in

Above: the Venus of Willendorf (Austria). Below: bas-relief Venus of Laussel (Dordogne, France).

these works has never been surpassed. There can equally be no doubt that the extraordinary works of art to be found in virtually all African and Melanesian (not to mention other) cultures have never been bettered in both sophistication and skill.

The art of prehistoric man appears also to have been highly stylized and frequently carried out with consummate skill. Among the best known works of prehistoric art are the wall and roof paintings discovered in 1940 at Lascaux, above the Vézère Valley, in central France. Though of mixed quality, many of the paintings are carried out with effectiveness and brio, and the whole performance conveys an overwhelming impress of the sheer amount of *life*. Some individual paintings in this cave are superb. The Lascaux cave paintings are almost certainly of Gravettian age and date back about 20,000 years from the present.

Judging from the large number of decorated caves found in cen-

Ivory music horn, Mangbetu, Belgian Congo.

tral France and southwestern Spain art was a much encouraged and valued skill. There is evidence that in this prehistoric period there were several art schools in existence in which training was provided for would-be artists. For example, at Genière, in central France, there was found in 1926 a small slab of limestone on which the figure of a bison was beautifully engraved. This is identically reproduced in the very individually painted polychrome of a bison on the wall of the cave at Font-de-Gaume, in the Dordogne, some two hundred miles distant.

The magico-religious purposes for which prehistoric man presumably developed cave art are still practiced in much the same way by many nonliterate peoples, that is, as a means of ensuring the food supply. The "fertility figures" of prehistoric man also, it is presumed, served such a utilitarian purpose. Other purposes to which the artist has devoted his skill have been the creation of fetishes, talismans, crests, representations of supernaturals, and the like. And art for art's sake is not entirely unknown in nonliterate societies and is not incompatible with the practical uses to which the artist's work might be put.

Literature

The literature of nonliterate peoples is, of course, unwritten. As the work of the imagination uttered in words, it is carried in the memory and handed down from generation to generation. In many cases, certain stories are considered to be the property of a particular individual who has inherited them by right of descent. Both prose and poetic forms are universal. A frequent form of storytelling is the group story, as in the Anansi stories of West Africa, in which all the members of the group who happen to be present participate, adding new and amusing gambits to the doings of a clever spider. Both the poetry and prose are often of great beauty.

In nonliterate societies poem and story serve very practical purposes in addition to the sheer pleasure they often provide, for they serve to preserve the traditions of the group, its history and achievements, providing opportunities for the participation in dramatic experiences, even if vicariously, and for the general enlargement of experience and increase in knowledge.

Music and the Dance

Every people has its music, musical instruments, songs, and

146

dances. These, too, may be privately owned, but in general are freely at the disposal of the people. Everywhere music and the dance are closely related, and only rarely is dancing unaccompanied by instrumental music. The music tends to be simple, but the dance is often highly elaborate and symbolic. Usually the sexes involved in the same dance, while dancing opposite each other, remain separated, there being no physical contact between them, a situation which has come about in the contemporary "Twist."

The highly elaborate dances of most nonliterate peoples often serve magico-religious purposes, as in the food-increase ceremonies. Since everywhere the intensely emotional value of music and dance is recognized, these activities enter into all those social situations which involve heightened effects, and thus serve to elicit intense emotional responses.

Conclusion

We have now come to the end of our brief survey of man and his works. What, if any, are some of the lessons to be drawn from this overview of man's incomparably variegated and adventuresome journey?

Above all we have learned that mankind is characterized by a fundamental likeness and unity. That the differences, both physical and cultural, that distinguish the various peoples of the earth, interesting and valuable as they are, are far outweighed by the fundamental likenesses, and that there is nothing in these differences which, in the scale of human values, renders any one of these peoples of less value or importance than the other. That the differences which exist between peoples are due to the operation of physical, genetic, and cultural factors which are largely the result of historical accidents of migration and isolation. We have found that if there exist any genetic bases for behavioral differences between any of the peoples of the world, these are probably of an

148

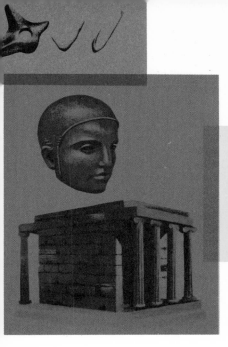

insignificant nature because of the peculiar evolutionary history of man. This evolutionary history has largely placed a premium upon the traits of co-operation, plasticity, and educability. It has not demanded of one group as compared with another any other special traits which in the course of evolution would have accumulated sufficient genetic difference to distinguish one from the other behaviorally in any major way. So that if and when the great experiment takes place in which all peoples will be given opportunities to participate in the world's work on a basis of political equality, we may fully expect that every people will have its contribution to make. Until that time we must learn to understand and respect the differences which distinguish the peoples of the earth and value them for what they are: each people's successful attempt to adjust to and master the environment in which they have found themselves. Some have been luckier than others; some have had a much harder time than others; some have been excluded from the advantages enjoyed by others; but all have more than managed to hold their own under the difficult conditions which have been the lot of every people, and almost everywhere to emerge triumphant.

Some of those whose triumphs did not endure perished not as a consequence of their inability to meet the challenges of the physical environment, but as a result of their inability to meet the superior force of alien invaders and the culturally disintegrating effects of a superimposed and unsympathetic foreign culture. Within the recent historic period the Tasmanians were exterminated in this manner, the Indian civilizations of the Americas destroyed, the peoples of the Pacific devastated, and the cultures of Australian aborigines and of many Eskimo groups ruined. American Indians and Negroes in the United States are still treated as second-class citizens, and in Angola and South Africa millions of Negroes are disfranchised in their own lands. If some of the things set out in this little book will help the reader to appreciate the common brotherhood of man, and to make it possible, insofar as he is able, for all men to enjoy the full development of their potentialities without impediment, the journey we have taken together will not have been in vain. Spanning the millennia we shall say with Terence, the Roman poet, I am a man, and nothing human is alien to me.

Index

Index